JOHN L. RAMSEY

LAURA J. RAMSEY

Published by: Boa Vista Press
                     800 Fifth Ave #151
                     Seattle, WA 98104

Printed by: Valco Graphics, Inc.
                     480 Andover Park E.
                     Seattle, WA 98188

Copyright Attorney: Carl G. Dowrey

THE GEM COLLECTOR'S HANDBOOK

Boa Vista Press

Acknowledgements

For help in preparing this manuscript we would like to thank:

Shelley French, Claudia Jones, Ken Jones, and Donna Lawrence.

To Family and Friends, with Love

THE GEM COLLECTOR'S HANDBOOK

CONTENTS

INTRODUCTION

Laura and I have spent most of our professional lives cloistered in the somewhat parochial society of gem dealers. However, we have been lucky enough to spend some time in the company of retail customers as well. People who do not know the intricacies of gems, minerals, and jewelry. From these fortunate encounters we have learned that there are certain questions most people seem to have as regards our chosen vocation. After enough years we have become aware which of these questions are most persistent and which are seemingly most important to consumers. It is to these questions that we address this book. Virtually everybody, it seems, likes, loves and is excited by the natural treasures we know as "gemstones." Since at least part of this positive emotive state is generated by the rarity of gem producing minerals it is no wonder that the average person has only a sketchy knowledge of what gems exist, what they look like, and where they can be purchased. Rare things, almost by definition, are hard to find out about.

This brings us to the fact that while it may be difficult to access information about gems, most information about gems is easy reading. The mineralogy involved with gems can be dry reading but that is the worst it gets. As science goes, gemology is both interesting and understandable. As for the history of gems, gem mining, and jewelry the reading is full of romance, intrigue, and exotic locations.

Our goal with this book is to give the reader factual answers to the questions they may have, to let the reader realize that the mysteries of gems can be untangled, and through the photographs have a sense of the beauty available in these small natural wonders.

John L. Ramsey
Washington State
11/15/94

I

COMING TO GRIPS WITH COLOR

For the collector learning to evaluate gems, color is perhaps the single most important area of concentration. Yet color can be one of the most elusive factors when learning the value of gems. The wisecrack about color goes: "Rubies are red, sapphires are blue, and emeralds are green - the redder, the bluer, the greener, the better." Giving out that much information can be likened to throwing a person a life preserver in a stormy ocean when a 1,000 foot ship underfoot would be more reassuring.

The size of the problem becomes especially apparent when we consider the number of species of stones and the number of color varieties within each species. Another problem arises from the subtleties of color involved in pricing gems. You will never know how many colors of blue there are until you start shopping for sapphires, especially fine sapphires. Commercial quality stones seem easier to grade in an orderly manner. However, nature produces so few top quality gems that in the topmost qualities there are almost always trade-offs when considering the color of one gem versus another.

One additional problem comes into play from considering only the better quality of stones. By diminishing the number of qualifying gems we find it increasingly difficult to comparison shop accurately. This is especially true of the rarer varieties of gemstones. For example, even an experienced, full-time dealer who decides to specialize in alexandrite may have to stumble and stub his toes for a year or two before he learns all he needs to know about the color of alexandrite. Alexandrite's rarity limits the opportunities of seeing truly fine stones. Thus, the gathering of knowledge takes a long time. Alexandrite may be an extreme example, but any qualifier, whether it be "alexandrite" or "better quality" tends to reduce the number of gems that are useful in learning what you need to know about color.

Additional problems arise because nature virtually never makes pure colors -- a point made by most art teachers. Since the crystalline materials fashioned into gems are made by nature, they seldom are pure in color. When we attempt to evaluate the color of a gem, our attempted description tries to tell some very subtle properties of the gem. By comparison, when we describe the clarity of a stone we can say it contains no inclusions or we can say it has inclusions. However, if we were to try to describe the clarity of an included stone with the same precision with which we try to describe color, we find variations in the attempt to describe clarity. For instance, a long inclusion might variously be described as needle-like, tubular, rod-like, cylindrical, or threadlike. Such accuracy of description does not matter with inclusions but does matter with color. The existence or non-existence of inclusions and their general size is all that matters with inclusions. But, with color the subtle differences we see make huge amounts of dollar differences. Color is the single most important factor in the four "C's". Subtle color differences equivalent to distinguishing between rod-like or thread-like inclusions do make dollar differences and are recognized in the trade. When we ask what is the color of a given gem we can seldom answer red, green, blue, or yellow, and be accurate. Realistically, we are asking what are the *colors* in a gem; which is most predominant and by how much. The predominant color of a given stone may be red, blue, or green (a mixed color itself), but there are always primary and secondary overtones present which affect the price more than any other factor in stone evaluation.

THE COLOR GRADING OF COLORED STONES

All of the grading systems for colored stones are relatively new and most of them could be classified as experimental. As yet the jury is still out as to which system is the best and which system will prevail as time goes on. However, it is our opinion that the GIA system will inevitably become the industry standard. The obvious reasons for that are several years of research and thousands of man-hours of time that went into formulating the system. The fact that the GIA*(see page 25) is a non-profit institution with third party impartiality is another reason. Another not so obvious reason, in our opinion, will be the fact that their system is open to every interested person and not guarded for their use only. All persons interested in colored stones need access to a viable, well-accepted system.

IN THE MEANTIME

While you may presently not have the time to take one of the GIA's courses you still need to become familiar with color as it relates to gemstones. The following few pages give some basic information that will help you understand color in gems.

SENSITIZATION:
THE LEXICON OF COLOR

Because colors occur in a mixed state in gemstones, we must first understand a little about both color theory and color mixing. This understanding represents a first step in a process we have decided to call sensitization. In order to understand and comprehend color we must be sensitive to it physically and be able to describe what we see. The ability to describe color will come to us by establishing a lexicon of color as applied to gemstones. People need words on which to hang their perceptions. This is especially true of the subtle experiences found in gems such as color variation, mixing, and overtones. Without a proper set of words we cannot discuss with other people what it is we see. Without the words we tend to dismiss what our eyes try to tell us. You would be surprised to see how slow and tentative people are when you show them a stone and ask its color, especially if they know you do not mean the obvious predominant color and are really trying to pin them down. You would think 90% of the population was color blind. Since most people are not schooled in color they are at a loss for the proper words to use, which in turn makes them unsure of what they see and what to say. Further, this lack of education seems to breed a difference of opinion in what they do see. Or perhaps they say what they see differently. It can take a group of serious-minded adults five or ten minutes to decide the color of a given stone.

We find a different group of people in the fraternity of experienced gem dealers. In order to survive at the dealer level a person has to become sensitive to color. A dealer who lacks color sensitivity would go broke in a big hurry. He would be unable to know a good buy from a bad buy, would almost certainly pay too much for his merchandise, and be unable to know his customers' needs. There are other problems he might have, but these three alone are enough to pave the road to the poorhouse. In contrast, the dealer who is naturally sensitive to color cuts his learning time to a minimum, avoids a few bad buys and generally becomes prosperous more quickly than his peers. The preponderance of dealers falls between these two extremes. They learn at an average pace and after some time in the trade become quite color sensitive.

Even so, some experienced dealers are noticeably more sensitive to color than others. After dealing with people over a period of years it becomes apparent that one dealer's telephone description will be accurate; another's so-so; and the third a definite, "I'll have to see it myself." If the majority of dealers learns at an average rate, this may be due to the fact that their learning is mostly "seat-of-the-pants." No schools exist for gem dealers. No other dealers are going to help them. No clear-cut path or set of instructions is set up to guide them. While that may be true for dealers, there is no reason for you, the collector, to stay in the dark. By becoming sensitive to colors you can save yourself time.

By understanding color you will grasp the concepts very quickly. By having a road map to color, you will reach a high level of color proficiency very quickly. By realizing the importance of color, you will feel the motivation to learn color from the beginning.

PRIMARY COLORS

Since gems by nature have mixed colors, we must learn about the mixing of colors. The first part of the lexicon we all already know -- the phrase, "primary colors." We all know that the primary colors are red, blue, and yellow and all other colors derive from them. Understanding the bare bones of mixing these three colors will help a great deal in understanding what we see. In an attempt to explain verbally, gem dealers often come up with fanciful terms: gunmetal blue, electric blue, peacock blue...the list goes on and on. However, by understanding a little color mixing theory we can cut through the jargon and be aware that a stone might be predominantly one color, with secondary overtones of "X" and tertiary overtones of "Y."

"Primary Colors" = red, yellow and blue. The colors from which all other colors are derived.

HUE

The very first word we need to learn is "hue." Although the word "hue" can be synonymous with the word "color," for our purposes, in order to lessen confusion, we will consider "hue" by itself.

The word "hue" denotes a *particular* color: "What hue is that ruby?" "Red" hopefully is the response. Using the word hue when discussing a *particular* color causes less confusion. In consequence, when we want to single out a characteristic of a particular stone called red, blue, or purple, we refer to its color *name* as the "hue." One important reason for using the word "hue" is to single out the *name* of the color as opposed to including the other properties of color such as how light or dark the color may be, or how pure the color is.

"Hue" = the name of a color: red, yellow, blue, green, etc. The attribute by which a color is distinguished from black, white, neutral gray.

VALUE

While most of us are somewhat familiar with the word hue, our next word "value" has more familiarity in its financial function. The value of a particular color has to do with the lightness or darkness of the particular color. The most common and easiest way to grasp color value is to think in terms of the black, white, and gray colors in a black and white photograph or black and white television picture. For every color seen in a color photograph there is an equivalent "value" in a black and white photograph. In the same sense any television picture broadcast can be picked up by either a color or a black and white set. If you put two TV sets together you can see that each color displayed on a color set translates into an equivalent value of black, white, or gray on a black and white set.

SHADE

In some usages the work "shade" is sometimes synonymous with "value." One color can be said to be two shades darker or lighter than another. However, rather than considering "shade" as a synonym of value, we propose that the word "shade" be used to refer to increments within the concept of value. The word "shade," unfortunately, tends to be very unscientific, very subjective, but very necessary. Perhaps one day when scientists have quantified color completely, the word "shade" will denote specific increments. But, in the meantime, we can use "shade" for our own purposes and know what *we* mean when *we* use it. So, when you see a stone you will know if it is the perfect shade for you or whether it is three shades too light or a couple of shades too dark.

"Shade" = increments of value in terms of lightness and darkness.

COLORLESS

Since our discussion of color revolves around gemstones, we must bring up the word "colorless." Colorless is the transparent version of white. A "colorless" stone allows all colors of light to pass through it equally. We know light passes through equally because a colorless stone breaks the light into all the colors of the rainbow. Diamond is the most commonly known gem that approaches colorlessness.

"Colorless" = in gems, allowing all colors of light to pass through the object, equally.

SATURATION

Saturation as a concept has a particular interest to those people interested in gems. In a general sense, saturated colors are preferred in the gem world. The state of saturation is the state of being completely filled. The idea of being completely filled implies that no room exists for anything else. A saturated color therefore can be described as one which is both intense (completely filled) and pure (room for no other color). A saturated gem represents the optimum. A gem whose color is not saturated is discounted from that optimum. A case in point are the gradings given to fancy diamonds which in the case of yellow run: light fancy yellow, fancy yellow, intense fancy yellow. In addition, notations are made as to the overtones, if any, such as: brownish yellow, greenish yellow, or grayish yellow. The optimum for a yellow diamond occurs when the stone has the intense label and no overtones -- a diamond with saturated color. Therefore, we can say a top grade yellow diamond is one which has a saturated color and be correct. We can also say a top grade blue sapphire is one which has a saturated color and also be correct.

One word of caution is necessary. There are gems whose color is too dark, especially in certain varieties of species, (i.e., green tourmaline, red garnets). The key to distinguishing between a nicely saturated color and a too dark color is a matter of practice and judgment. In the field of gemstones the use of the word "saturated" should be used to denote the state of intensity and purity of color combined.

"Saturation" = the state of being completely full of one particular hue.

PLEOCHROISM

Another word from the existing gemological lexicon is "pleochroism." A pleochroic stone exhibits more than one color or shade of a color quite distinctly. As opposed to the way diamonds disperse light into colors, pleochroic stones show more than one color even when the colors seen are neither reflected nor refracted colors. The crystalline formation of a particular mineral causes pleochroism in cut gems.

We can break pleochroism into two distinct varieties -- the most common being "*di*chroism." For those familiar with prefixes, we know the "*di*" of *di*chroism means there are two colors in a dichroic stone. Commonly known dichroic stones are: ruby, sapphire, emerald, aquamarine, topaz, amethyst (quartz), tourmaline and peridot.

"*Tri*chroism" is the second and less common form of pleochroism. For those of us who rode *tri*cycles when young we know a *tri*chroic stone has three colors. The gems falling into this category, while less well known, include alexandrite, kunzite, and andalusite.

Pleochroism must be distinguished from another type of phenomenon that displays more than one color. We call this phenomenon "color zoning." A pleochroic stone will display more than one color no matter how many times it is cut. For example, if a 20 carat andalusite were cut into 20 one carat stones, each piece would display pleochroism. In contrast, a color zoned stone, such as a bi-colored tourmaline, can be cut in such a way as to have two distinct pieces, each of a distinctly different color.

"Pleochroism" = exhibiting more than one color or shade of a color due to the crystalline structure of the variety of gem being examined.

BODY COLOR

The term "body color" used in the gem trade refers to a gem's color without reflection. In many cases the monetary worth of a given gem can best be determined by assessing the body color. In a windowed stone this can be done by looking down through the table into the area minus reflection. The color you see in that area is the "body color."

In a more hopeful situation, with a well-cut stone we can determine "body color" by turning the stone upside down. When turned over, gems do not exhibit as much in the way of reflection or refraction; the color you see being abstracted from other optical properties of the gem is the "body color." Intense reflection or refraction can mask the true "body color." Determining body color helps a potential buyer in his dollar evaluation.

"Body Color" = the color of a gem when viewed without reflection or refraction.

OVERTONE

For our purposes, the word "overtone" will refer to a color or colors in addition to the main color of a stone. For example, most rubies exhibit colors in addition to red. The additional colors may be purple, pink, orange or brown. There may be one of these colors or several and they may vary as to what percentage they make up of the total observable color. There may be a great deal of purple and very little orange. In such a case the predominant overtone is purple and the secondary overtone is orange. In most gem varieties, very pure colors are usually the optimum. However in other varieties the overtones are considered to be attractive and will not cause a discount and may even bring a premium. Learn to read the overtones of the gems at which you look. It will help you become more sensitive to color and learn to evaluate the worth of stones more easily.

"Overtone" = the ancillary colors observable in a stone that modify the main color.

ANALYZING COLOR IN A CHOSEN GEMSTONE

Armed with our new vocabulary and awareness of color we can begin looking at gemstones offered for sale and evaluate their color. We do this by asking a series of questions.

1. *What color is our stone?*
   At this point you should be looking at the stone to determine the predominant hue of the body color. If the body color has a name you come up with, give it that label.

2. *What are the overtones, if any?*
   After you have named the predominant color, try to determine the overtones and ask yourself if they are heavy overtones or light overtones? Do they modify the predominant hue a great deal or just a little?

3. *In terms of color value, is this gem light, medium, or dark?*

4. *In terms of saturation, is this tone a good strong, pure: red...blue...green...pink?*

5. *Ask about shade if you are looking at more than one stone of the same kind in terms of lighter or darker -- one stone as opposed to the other. Which shade do you prefer? Which shade is prettier? Which shade is considered better by the experts?*

6. *Can I see any pleochroism in this stone? Does it enhance or detract from the stone? What do experts consider most desirable regarding pleochroism in this species?*
   Keep in mind that some pleochroic stones show their pleochroism more than others and in certain stones pleochroism can be considered either a plus or a minus, while in others it makes no difference.

The main objective in understanding color and asking and answering questions about a particular stone is for you to be able to make decisions based on what you observe. The more you consciously sensitize yourself to color, the more confident you will become in making decisions. Also, you will be able to discuss what you see with others, be they friends, relatives, or strangers. Most importantly, this knowledge enables you to hold your own with the vendor of the stone.

MIXING COLORS

Now that we have our own color lexicon, we can discuss the mixing of colors. By mixing the three primary colors...red, blue, and yellow, we get secondary colors. Red and blue make purple. Red and yellow make orange. Blue and yellow make green.

Changing the value makes other name colors. Light red becomes pink. Artists make pink by adding white to red. Lavender is purple that has been similarly treated. *Color balance* can create name colors as well. For instance, chartreuse is green with a great deal more yellow than blue. Chartreuse is simply a green that has so much more of one color than the other that it has both a distinct look and name.

However, when we examine stone species and their colors, we quickly exhaust the name colors: red, yellow, blue, green, violet, orange, pink, and chartreuse. For the rest of the other colors we encounter we must make up names. For instance, when we say "Imperial topaz" we mean a stone composed of gold/yellow and orange with a hint of pink. "Aquamarine" stands for the name of both a beryl variety gemstone and the name of its own color. "Aquamarine" illustrates a very good example of how, in order to describe gem colors, it becomes necessary to find a common denominator in nature to point to and say -- "That is the color." "Aquamarine" has a connotation of a blue hue with just a hint of green, with a color value as well. The color value of aquamarine is not too dark, much as the sea is normally not too dark.

The lesson of aquamarine helps to point out the type of thinking necessary when dealing with color in gems. While the gem market has assessed the general color of aquamarine, it will be your responsibility to examine each stone offered and decide upon its color.

*(From page 13) The GIA or Gemological Institute of America is a non-profit educational and research institution for gems and jewelry. It is currently located in Santa Monica, California. For further explanation see Education chapter page 58.

OVERTONE CHARTS

The following is a chart showing overtones certain gemstones are likely to have.

NAME OF GEMSTONE	OVERTONES	CLASSIFICATION
ALEXANDRITE		
[Red phase]	+gray	bad
	+brown	bad
	+blue	acceptable
[Green phase]	+gray	bad
	+brown	bad
	+blue	acceptable
	+yellow	undesirable
ANDALUSITE		
	+red	good
	+gray	bad
	+pink	good
BERYL		
[Aquamarine]	+yellow	bad
	+brown	bad
	+gray	bad
[Emerald]	+blue	good except in excess (Colombian "look")
	+yellow	good except in excess (Russian "look")
	+brown	bad
	+gray	bad

CHRYSOBERYL

[Yellow]	+brown	undesirable
	+gray	undesirable
[Pure Green]	+brown	undesirable
	+gray	undesirable
[Chartreuse]	+brown	undesirable
	+gray	undesirable

DIAMOND

[Colorless]	+yellow	bad
	+brown	bad
	+gray	bad
	+blue	good
	+pink	good

[Canary]   Any deviation *from* yellow is bad

[Pink]   Hot pink is created by a blue overtone but if overly prevalent turns the pink into lavender.

[Blue]   Any deviation from blue is bad.

GROSSULAR GARNET

[Tsavorite]

Pure Green	+blue	good optimum color
	+yellow	bad
	+brown	bad
	+gray	bad
[Orange]	+yellow	bad
	+brown	bad
	+gray	bad
	+red	good if not in excess

PERIDOT

[Green]	+brown	bad
	+gray	bad

RHODOLITE GARNET

[Red/Purple and Red/Pink]		
	+brown	bad
	+gray	bad
	+blue	good
	+orange	bad

RUBY

[Red]	+blue	very, very slight is good any more is bad
	+gray	bad
	+brown	bad
	+yellow	bad
	+pink	slight can be acceptable but not desirable; too much and it is no longer ruby, but sapphire.

SAPPHIRE

[Blue]		any deviation from blue is not desirable
	+purple	can be acceptable but not desirable
	+brown	bad
	+green	bad
	+gray	bad
[Yellow-Gold]	+brown	bad
	+green	bad
	+orange	good
[Pink]	+blue	good but not in excess
	+gray	bad
	+brown	bad
	+yellow	bad

SPESSARTITE GARNET

[Orange]	+red	acceptable but not desirable
	+yellow	bad
	+brown	bad but stone may be acceptable

SPINEL

[Red Spinel]	+brown	bad
	+gray	bad
	+blue	good except in excess
	+yellow	bad
[Blue Spinel]	+gray	bad
	+purple	acceptable in minute amounts but not desirable
[Orange (Flame)]	+brown	bad
	+red	acceptable
	+gray	bad
[Purple & Lavender Spinel]	+brown	bad
	+gray	bad
	+pink	good
	+blue	good
	+green	bad

SPODUMENE (Kunzite)

[Pink or Purple]	+yellow	bad
	+gray	bad

TANZANITE

[Blue]	+brown	bad
	+gray	bad
	+purple	acceptable but not preferable

IMPERIAL TOPAZ

[Yellow, Orange & Red]	+yellow	bad
	+brown	bad
	+gray	bad
	+pink	good
[Pink]	+yellow	bad
	+brown	bad
	+gray	bad
	+blue	good (hot pink)

[Green]

Pure Green	+yellow	undesirable
	+blue	good
	+brown	bad
	+gray	bad

Blue-Green	+yellow	bad in excess
	+brown	bad
	+gray	bad

Chrome-Green	+yellow	bad
	+brown	bad
	+gray	bad
	+blue	good

[Pink]

Pure Pink	+yellow	bad
	+brown	bad
	+blue	good

Brown Pink	+gray	bad
	+yellow	bad
	+blue	good
	+gray	bad

[Rubellite]

Hot Pink	+yellow	bad
	+blue	good
	+brown	bad

Red	+gray	bad
	+yellow	bad
	+blue	good except in excess
	+brown	bad
	+gray	bad

[Bi-Colors]

Pink or Green	+yellow	bad
	+blue	good (hot pink)
	+brown	bad
	+gray	bad

TOURMALINE (cont.)

Red or Green	+yellow	bad
	+blue	good
	+brown	bad
	+gray	bad
[Indicolite (Blue Tourmaline)]		
Blue	+brown	bad
	+gray	bad

ZIRCON

[Red to Brown]	+yellow	bad
	+gray	bad
	+green	bad
	+red	good
[Blue]	+brown	bad
	+gray	bad
	+yellow	bad
	+green	bad

II

GEMS AND JEWELRY

SOME NOTES ON JEWELRY, JEWELRY DESIGN, JEWELRY CARE

While most of this book is dedicated strictly to gemstones it is obvious that most gemstones will wind up in some form of jewelry. A great number of our customers design their own jewelry from the gems they purchase. Whole books have been dedicated to the topic of jewelry design. However, in this book we have only the space of a single chapter in which to discuss the enjoyable enterprise of design. Since we have only the space of a single chapter it is not our intention to go into all the intricacies of jewelry design. Our goal is simply to give you some basic ideas and guidelines so that if the design bug happens to give you a bite you might have a bit of knowledge and the courage to go forth and design some wonderful jewelry. Designing is interesting and fun in a lot of ways in that it is an act of creation. It gives a person the chance to bring into being something which has not previously existed prior to the act of creation. In looking up the dictionary definition of design it is "to invent and bring into being". Designing can be easy for some. Certain people find the act of creation relatively easy.

While there are other people for whom creation is not a realistic alternative. It is our contention that most people fall somewhere in between these two extremes and that in fact more people would be creating more of their own jewelry designs given the opportunity to obtain the materials and to simply believe they are capable.

I THINK I CAN, I KNOW I CAN

One of the big aids in this venture is believing in yourself. We would like to encourage people to believe in their ability to design jewelry. We had an interesting occurrence not too long ago with a customer who had been buying some loose stones from us. She designed a pendant for her daughter. The starting point of the piece was a double triangle cut blue topaz in which she had visualized the sails of a sail boat. With the aid of a goldsmith a design was realized with a gold sail boat and blue topaz sails. It is a very effective design. However, in talking to her after the fact she indicated that despite all the compliments she got for the design work she decided to quit while she was ahead. In your own case even if you decide to design something only one time we believe that once is better than no times. But who knows, you may decide to make jewelry design a new hobby. For many of us design is every bit as much fun as collecting and owning loose gemstones.

WHAT'S EVERYBODY WEARING

Even before you sit down and attempt to put a design to paper there is a lot you can do to prepare yourself for that moment. The first thing you can do is to become observant about design. You can begin to look at other jewelry designs with a more critical eye. What do you see that you like? What do you see that you do not like? What specifically is it you see that you do and do not like? It is virtually impossible to be out and about in the company of people and not see jewelry. Jewelry is so basic to our society that virtually everybody wears some kind of jewelry. Of course there is the old standby--the mall. Almost everybody goes to shopping centers where you can observe not only the jewelry in the store windows but also the jewelry worn by the mall patrons themselves. So, jewelry is all around us. The opportunity to see what we like and do not like is there.

You can begin to categorize your observations. There are sizes, shapes, colors, textures. Observe if there is movement in the pieces you notice -- especially neck wear. See about the balance and proportion of the pieces you observe. During the observing phase you can begin to discern what your general likes and dislikes are.

WHAT JEWELRY HAS MEANT IN THE PAST -- WHAT JEWELRY MAY MEAN TO YOU

However, before we go too far into the design process itself perhaps we should go into jewelry itself and what jewelry has meant to mankind through the millennia. The passage of time has denied us the opportunity to see the first person who made a piece of jewelry. We cannot go back in time and see that very special moment. Yet we do know from the records of archeology that mankind has been regularly creating jewelry for the past 7,000 years. Now that is a tradition! In the earliest years of jewelry fabrication we are not sure what the motive was for its use. However, there is reason to believe that the use of jewelry as amulets (protection) goes back at least 5,000 years. In the belief systems of those times specific powers were ascribed to specific objects. The idea of an amulet was to obtain the ascribed power by wearing the object.

WHY DO WE WEAR JEWELRY

It is interesting to ponder the reason that we do wear jewelry. If this has been going on for 7,000 years and possibly longer then the use of jewelry must be significant to human beings. An important thing to note about jewelry is that it is something we wear. While not indispensable to our comfort, as is clothing, the use of jewelry has remained in the society of man and shows no sign of becoming less popular--rather the opposite. The fact that we use jewelry to adorn our bodies makes jewelry very personal. While current use of jewelry stems more from esthetic motives rather than from a desire for mystical properties there are a number of very personal motivations for wearing jewelry.

A SYMBOL OF LOVE

In current times one of the strongest motives for wearing jewelry has to do with sentimental reasons. The durability of jewelry helps us mark and keep a special moment with us through time. This is especially true of certain times that are considered rites of passage. At special moments in our lives we can expect to receive gifts of jewelry. The most revered current custom is the engagement ring. In this instance a piece of jewelry helps mark the passage from being a single unmarried person to becoming a married person. The gift of a mixture of precious metal and precious stone, which are rare items and expensive items, is a demonstration of the love and esteem of the giver. The durability of the jewelry gift is a symbol of the unending nature of love. Of course there are other times when a gift of jewelry is expected. Almost everybody has a high school ring that marks the graduation from school. And then of course there are the various years during a marriage where a gift of jewelry is considered appropriate. Jewelry then can be considered an integral part of our social fabric.

A PERSONAL REWARD

In addition to sentimental reasons for wearing jewelry that are social to a degree, there are other more personal reasons for wearing jewelry. Amongst other things jewelry can be considered a reward to oneself. At times we need to put into physical, tangible terms the need for a reward for the ongoing battles of everyday life. The precious nature of the materials from which jewelry is made is something we have a craving to make part of our own lives. To own and possess beauty gives us the gratification we may need to do our daily grind--to get up early to take care of the kids, to get up and go to work, to, as Shakespeare so eloquently had Hamlet say "suffer the slings and arrows of outrageous fortune". Whether the slings and arrows are as outlandish as those put upon Hamlet or simply getting cut off from a parking space at the super-market. Jewelry as a reward is attractive at least in part due to its enduring nature. Of course we have other material rewards for ourselves but many of them either require extensive maintenance, or simply do not last long by their very nature. In contrast, quality jewelry can last a lifetime with minimal maintenance and even become, through bequest, part of an ongoing family tradition. The desire to have something permanent in a world of impermanence and transience is understandable.

FASHION AND OUR PERSONALITY

Since jewelry is used for adornment it also becomes a fashion statement. The history of fashion (apparel) is incomplete without a history of jewelry as well. As we go through time jewelry has its own fashion trends. As such the jewelry we choose to wear is as much a statement about ourselves as is the clothing we wear or the car we drive. In a sense there is a whole chain of events beginning with personal adornment and leading on to design. Starting with the notion of personal adornment a person is going to want to make his/her personal adornment consistent with his/her sense of fashion. His/her personal sense of fashion is going to lead to his/her own personal sense of style. When a person has an awareness of their own sense of style their design work will naturally tend to include certain types of designs and leave out others.

ARE YOU BOLD? ARE YOU SHY?

A lot of these elements should be considered together as part of the design process. Our sense of fashion and style helps to define our personality just as our personality helps to define our sense of fashion and style. People can be bold, spirited, shy, feminine. Jewelry can be bold, spirited, shy, feminine -- any of the characteristics we would like to assign to personality. Everybody has a sense of style that tells us secrets about their personality. At times we want to communicate these things about ourselves to others through physical, tangible means such as clothing or jewelry. At other times we use our sense of style to change things about our personality. Perhaps if we perceive ourselves to be too shy we might want to communicate a hidden sense of boldness through our personal adornment. Perhaps a person might perceive themselves as being too bold and might want to tone down their projected image through their sense of style.

BEYOND FASHION: A PERSONAL SENSE OF STYLE

In addition to our sense of fashion due to our personality we can get into certain categories that already exist within the jewelry world. Categories that might evoke a sense of recognition are: casual, romantic, classic-traditional, ethnic, historical. Whether we are aware of it or not each of us has our own personal sense of style, partly based on our personality, partly based on our sense of esthetics, partly based on our sense of social standing. There are literally thousands of products available to us on a daily basis that can affect our personal style. These products are comprised of many categories, from make-up, apparel, or scents, to jewelry. These products when taken as a whole become a rather full expression of ourselves and are a sign of our own preferred style. While we may belong to a particular social or ethnic group and have in a sense defined our personal style broadly along those lines, each individual has their own very specific style that is their own. The point of this is that when you are designing your own jewelry, in addition to observing outwardly, it is good to look at one's own style. It is good if possible to look at oneself from a more objective standpoint in order to assess one's overall look. What is it we've been working toward all these years with all the choices we've made from all the products we've mentioned. Despite all the choices available a person tends to find themselves opting for a few of the available choices. We do this on a regular basis and create a pattern. For instance, buying only a few of the available perfumes and leaving the other ones alone. In terms of makeup, people find themselves using certain colors and certain products and leaving others alone. The same holds true for clothing. People tend to shop at certain stores and not go into other stores. This even gets specific enough that a person may shop only in certain departments of a given store and not go into the other departments.

Through years and years of experimentation each of us comes to a point of having our own style. So, when it comes to the act of creating, our own designs should somehow reflect the sense of style that we have and with which we are comfortable. On the other hand our designs might want to reflect a sense of style to which we aspire. In either case it makes sense to know enough about ones existing sense of style in order to be consistent with it or to move away from it in a controlled manner. This will help us make creations with which we are satisfied in the long run. Self evaluation with regards to style can help us figure out what it is we like about what we've been doing and what we do not like about our past choices.

BUILDING YOUR JEWELRY WARDROBE

In addition to evaluating your personal sense of style and how it is involved with your personality another issue is your jewelry wardrobe. Undoubtedly you already have a jewelry wardrobe. Of course, those of us who love gems and jewelry always consider the state of our jewelry wardrobe to be incomplete. There is always something new and wonderful just around the corner. However, a certain amount of evaluation here can help in the design process.

A look at one's lifestyle can be a help in creating a useful jewelry collection. Are you a traveler, a teacher, an artist, a home maker, an opera singer, a lawyer, a policeman, a flight attendant. Each of these lifestyles may require a different jewelry wardrobe. Then too, in addition to our vocation each of us has a certain amount of free time and certain patterns of how we spend that time. Appropriate choices to go with one's lifestyle can make jewelry more useable and functional. On the other hand we can get back to what we touched on before about making changes in ones life and using jewelry to facilitate those changes. Jewelry can be an incentive for yourself to make a change and an outward statement to others. Maybe there is a particular social event in which you would like to participate but never felt your jewelry wardrobe would stand the test. Perhaps your new jewelry designs can help change that for you. So we have not only the lifestyle you live but the lifestyle you aspire to as considerations.

LETS SEE WHAT WE'VE GOT

While you are looking over your jewelry wardrobe you might take the chance to evaluate your existing taste. This will give you insight to where you fit within existing categories. Do you like classical looking jewelry with simple symmetrical designs, a tailored and conservative look. Perhaps you like a romantic look with pearls, cameos, and antique jewelry. Then again, maybe your thirst for jewelry is quenched by a particular ethnic look. For example you may have designs inspired by the native American traditions. Possibly your look can be typified by what we call the contemporary look that features heavier gold and occasional asymmetrical designs. Looking at your existing wardrobe can help you take note of where your taste has been in the past and where you may want it to go in the future.

WHAT'S THE OCCASION

While you assess your lifestyle you may want to think about the various occasions in your life--your special occasions and your more ordinary occasions. When you design a jewelry piece you may want to consider for which occasions you wish to wear it. Do you want an especially fine piece for special events, do you want a multi-purpose piece to wear for a wide range of events, do you want a casual piece of daywear for your every day life.

NARROWING OUR FOCUS

Largely what we have been doing so far is a matter of narrowing our focus before we begin the design process. What we are attempting to do is to take the infinity of possibilities for design and through analysis and a narrowing of focus get down to specifics. We have addressed what jewelry means to us, our sense of style, our personality. All these items will tend to influence design each in their own way. They are, if you will, the mind of the artist.

Next we move on to the materials. These are, if you will, the artist's palette. Here we find a virtually endless number of combinations. In gem materials there are at least 30 different species and varieties from which to choose. Within each of those 30 there are many color variations. Many of the gem producing minerals produce color variants of which most people are unaware. For instance most people assume garnets are red. Well there are at least 20 different colors to be had in the minerals known as garnets. Imperial topaz comes in at least 5 easily distinguishable colors. Sapphire is available in a rainbow of colors. The only color it does not come in is red since red sapphire is known as ruby. The more you know about gems the more complete your palette. The color plates in this book alone show more colors and varieties of gems than the average person has an acquaintance with, and what we show here is the tip of the iceberg. Beyond color there is shape. The five basic shapes of gems are round, emerald cut, oval, marquise, and pear shape. There are also variations on each of these shapes available. Then there is also the issue of size. Gems come in some cases too big to afford. With all these variants there are easily 1500 different products that you can include in the gemstone part of your palette.

GOLD, SILVER, OR PLATINUM

In addition to the choices you have available in gems there are the choices you have available in metal. In gold alone there are a myriad of choices. There are choices of the fineness of the gold: 10K, 14K, 18K, 22K, and even 24K. Of course there are limitations within each of those choices as to how they look or how they may be used. However very special effects can be had through the gold choice. In addition to the special look each of the above choices offers there are special effects to be created through the alloying metals. Perhaps the best known of these are rose gold and white gold.

The white metals give us some other choices. Silver is affordable and fun to experiment with due to its affordability. When possible the rhodium plating of silver gives silver a special look in addition to making it less susceptible to oxidation. Platinum is a bit tricky to work with due to its high melting point but platinum jewelry carries an exotic aura and a sense of prestige that simply has to make the wearer feel special.

Considering all the gems available and with the metal choices available a jewelry designer has endless possibilities. With the process of analysis we outlined earlier your choices should follow an orderly route. Choices become more obvious and you become ready for the grand moment of creation.

THE DESIGN ITSELF

In addition to the personal and esthetic considerations we've been discussing there are some practical considerations to the designing of jewelry. Since jewelry is made to be worn it should be comfortable. A piece of jewelry that is not comfortable is a problem. Durability is an important issue as well. There are certain intricate designs that are beautiful to look at but which just will not stand up to being worn. Often this happens when the amount of the metal used is just too skimpy. Also a design may be beautiful on paper but simply too difficult to translate into a three dimensional confection of gold and gems. So, practicality, comfort, and wearability are considerations as well.

BEGINNING YOUR DRAWING

In bringing jewelry dreams into reality we have always found it best to commit those dreams to paper in the form of a drawing. It is possible to talk to your goldsmith until you are both hoarse but nothing speaks as eloquently as a drawing. While you have the paper in hand additional specifications cannot hurt. Specify the fineness of gold, and your ring size, if appropriate. Anything that can help you be as specific as possible will in turn help your goldsmith.

When it comes to the drawing itself take your time and do the best you can but do not be put off by lack of artistic talent. By and large a drawing for a piece of jewelry is similar to house plans which are non-artistic. Even if your drawing is crude it will show your intentions. Also, the patience to do and re-do a drawing can help.

Keep refining your project until you are satisfied. As a practical matter two views of the piece will help the goldsmith enormously (see illustration 1D). The two views that will help are a top view (plan view in architectural terms) and a side view. By doing a drawing a lot of factors come together. If you can make the drawing life size you will be able to see if the piece can in fact be done with the materials you have chosen.

LETS PLAY GEMS

One of the easiest and most practical methods for designing jewelry is to start with the gems. While gold can be molded, pulled, and hammered into virtually any shape your stones are the size and shape they are. To get ideas put your stones on a blank sheet of white paper. Turn each of the stones upside-down so it rests on the large table facet. If you have gem tweezers they will now prove their worth. This is especially effective if you are using more than one stone in a piece since you can put them in proximity almost as they will be in the finished piece. With the gems in close proximity it is easy to get a sense of size and proportion of the finished piece. In the case of surrounding a large stone with smaller stones you will see if you have enough of the little ones. You can also assess the color combinations you propose. In addition, this process is so easy and so entertaining you may feel like trying more than one combination and keep trying until you come up with exactly what you want.

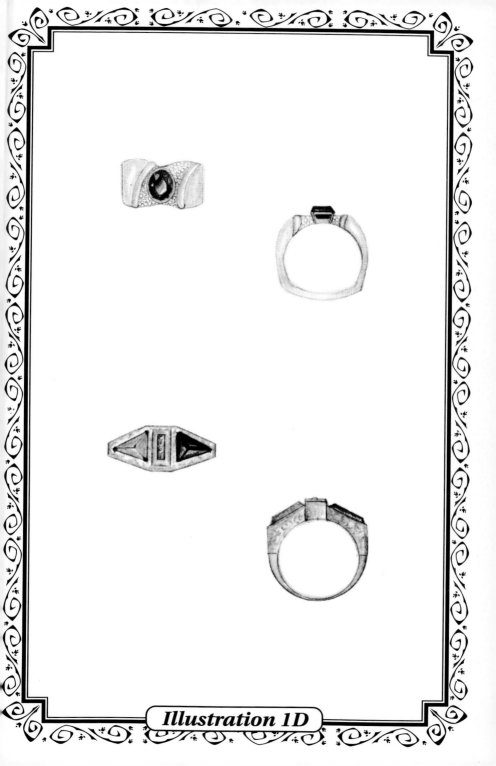

Illustration 1D

PUT YOUR BEST FACE FORWARD

Illustration 2D shows us several different face structures. When you are designing earrings it is a good idea to keep in mind some basic ideas regarding your face. We are all familiar with the idea of designing your hair in a way that is complimentary to your face. So it is no wonder that earrings should take into consideration the face as well. Shown in illustration 2D are four different facial types. Figures 1-4 each in turn represent round, square, oval, and long facial structures. The basic rule is to go opposite your face structure as follows:

1. Round face: With a round face you may want to design earrings that tend to lengthen and slenderize the look of your face. A longer earring that is narrow at the top should achieve this goal. Wide at the top would defeat this even with a longer type earring.

2. Square face: A square face presents a similar look in certain respects to a round face. At the top of an earring a square face can accommodate a little more width than a round face. However, the general goal is to lengthen.

3. Oval face: An oval face is considered somewhat of a neutral. Virtually any size of round earrings look good with the oval face. The proud owner of an oval face is allowed some more leeway than other facial structures but should perhaps not be as extreme in any direction as the round or long face.

Figure 1
ROUND

Figure 2
SQUARE

Figure 3
OVAL

Figure 4
LONG

Illustration 2D

4. Long face: In going the opposite from a long face you may want to use square or diamond shaped earrings. In this case larger than average earrings seem to make a complimentary statement as well.

LETTING GO -- DESIGNING FOR THE 90'S AND BEYOND

A last word on design that you might think about is the time, the era in which we live. While each generation considers itself "just the latest, newest, and most modern" it is true that times do change. The fact is that we are living in one of the least restrictive times when it comes to fashion of any kind. For the designer the less restrictions the better. There was a time when if you went out with pearls you simply had to be wearing gloves. There also seemed to be ridgid restrictions of how much jewelry you would wear at one time. Well, in this sense the bad old days are gone. Feel free to design what you like to please yourself. Today's grandmother can go beyond cameos and a 90's young adult might want to break the costume jewelry barrier. This is the point where your ongoing education for gems can come into play. Never before have so many different gem materials been available to so many people. By learning what is out there and available you can go beyond what you may have previously imagined.

Gem Sizing Chart

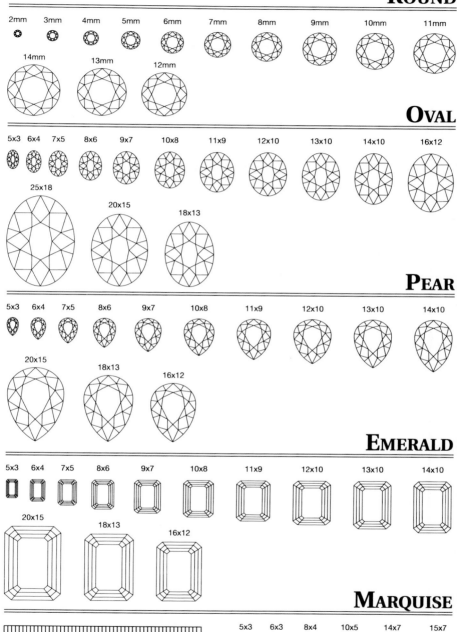

ROUND

2mm 3mm 4mm 5mm 6mm 7mm 8mm 9mm 10mm 11mm
14mm 13mm 12mm

OVAL

5x3 6x4 7x5 8x6 9x7 10x8 11x9 12x10 13x10 14x10 16x12
25x18 20x15 18x13

PEAR

5x3 6x4 7x5 8x6 9x7 10x8 11x9 12x10 13x10 14x10
20x15 18x13 16x12

EMERALD

5x3 6x4 7x5 8x6 9x7 10x8 11x9 12x10 13x10 14x10
20x15 18x13 16x12

MARQUISE

5x3 6x3 8x4 10x5 14x7 15x7

1 2 3 4 5

(scale 25mm = 1")

HARDNESS CHART

HARDNESS	GEMSTONE
10	Diamond
9	Ruby Sapphire
8½	Alexandrite Cat's Eye Chrysoberyl Chrysoberyl
8	Beryl (*7½ - 8) Spinel Topaz
7½	Andalusite Beryl (*7½ - 8) Iolite (*7 - 7½) Pyrope Garnet (*7 - 7½) Rhodolite Garnet (*7 - 7½) Spessartite Garnet (*7 - 7½) Tourmaline (*7 - 7½) Zircon
7	Demantoid Garnet (*6½ - 7) Grossular Garnet Hessonite Garnet Hiddenite Spodumene (*6 - 7) Iolite (*7 - 7½) Kunzite Spodumene (*6 - 7) Peridot (*6½ - 7) Pyrope Garnet (*7 - 7½) Quartz Rhodolite Garnet (*7 - 7½) Spessartite Garnet (*7 - 7½) Spodumene (*6 - 7) Tanzanite Zoisite (*6 - 7)

HARDNESS CHART (continued)

HARDNESS	GEMSTONE
7	Tourmaline (*7 - 7½) Tsavorite Garnet
6½	Demantoid Garnet (*6½ - 7) Hiddenite Spodumene (*6 - 7) Kunzite Spodumene (*6 - 7) Opal (*5 - 6½) Peridot (*6½ - 7) Scapolite Spodumene (*6 - 7) Tanzanite Zoisite (*6 - 7)
6	Diopside (*5 - 6) Hiddenite Spodumene (*6 - 7) Kunzite Spodumene (*6 - 7) Labradorite Feldspar Opal (*5 - 6½) Spodumene (*6 - 7) Tanzanite Zoisite (*6 - 7) Turquoise (*5 - 6)
5½	Diopside (*5 - 6) Opal (*5 - 6½) Turquoise (*5 - 6)
5	Diopside (*5 - 6) Opal (*5 - 6½) Turquoise (*5 - 6)
4½	Rhodochrosite (*3½ - 4½)

JEWELRY PROPERTIES

STONE	HARDNESS	REACTION TO STEAMING	REACTION TO ULTRASONIC
Diamond	H. 10	excellent	excellent
Ruby and Sapphire (Corundum)	H. 9	good	good
Catseye & Alexandrite (chrysoberyl)	H. 8½	good	good
Spinel	H. 8	good	good
Topaz	H. 8	bad	fair
Emerald (beryl)	H. 7½ - 8	poor	poor
Aquamarine (beryl)	H. 7½ - 8	fair	fair
Tourmaline	H. 7 - 7½	poor	fair
Garnet including Rhodolite & Tsavorite	H. 6½ - 7½	fair	good
Amethyst & Citrine (quartz)	H. 6½ - 7	fair	good
Peridot	H. 6½ - 7	fair	fair
Tanzanite (zoisite)	H. 6½	poor	poor
Kunzite & (spodumene)	H. 6 - 7	poor	fair
Zircon	H. 6 - 6½	poor	fair
Moonstone (feldspar)	H. 6 - 6½	fair	fair
Opal	H. 5½ - 6½	bad	bad
Turquoise	H. 5 - 6	fair	poor
Lapis Lazuli	H. 5 - 6	fair	fair

BIRTHSTONE CHART

The following is the list of birthstones for the months of the year.

Month	Birthstone	Alternate Stone
January	Garnet	
February	Amethyst	
March	Aquamarine	
April	Diamond	
May	Emerald	
June	Pearl	Alexandrite
July	Ruby	
August	Peridot	
September	Sapphire	
October	Opal	Tourmaline
November	Topaz	
December	Turquoise	Zircon

ANNIVERSARY GEMSTONE CHART

1	Gold Jewelry	13	Citrine
2	Garnet	14	Opal
3	Pearl	15	Ruby
4	Blue Topaz	20	Emerald
5	Sapphire	25	Silver Jubliee
6	Amethyst	30	Pearl Jubilee
7	Onyx	35	Emerald
8	Tourmaline	40	Ruby
9	Lapis Lazuli	45	Sapphire
10	Diamond Jewelry	50	Golden Jubilee
11	Turquoise	55	Alexandrite
12	Jade	60	Diamond Jubliee

III

EDUCATION

Over and over again, throughout this book we have emphasized the importance of knowledge and education in making the right gemstone purchase. As a collector you have two basic choices in initiating your acquisition. One alternative is to seek out a reputable and reliable source whom you trust implicitly. The other choice available to you is to enroll in any of the very fine courses offered by two of the more prominent educational gemological institutions. You may select courses in colored stones, diamonds, or both. Not only will the courses be beneficial to you as a collector but these courses are interesting and entertaining in and of themselves.

A realistic third alternative is to combine the first two alternatives. Becoming your own expert is the ideal, but for many people it is often impractical. Then too, the courses of education, although helpful, are not designed specifically for collectors. Practical education, attained by those who trade in gems, can take a great deal of time. Many collectors might be unable to spend this time. One of the best uses of gemological education for the collector is to evaluate suppliers. Competing against people in the gem trade is a less reasonable goal than working with them from the vantage point of a well educated collector.

As an introduction to the available educational opportunities, we would like to describe the courses offered by the Gemological Institute of America, and the Gemological Association of Great Britain.

Though these courses are not directly aimed at the gem collector, they do provide a unique opportunity for education. The courses offered by the two institutions we are showcasing are already very well thought of in the gem trade and jewelry industry. As a practical matter we would like to discuss these two courses in order of proximity. The GIA with two U.S. centers and home study offers the most easily accessible course.

THE GEMOLOGICAL INSTITUTE OF AMERICA

The Gemological Institute of America (GIA) has been in existence since 1930 when it was founded by Robert M. Shipley, a jeweler, who wrote the first home study course on the subject of classification and evaluation of gemstones.

During the next ten years the correspondence program reached completion. Research and testing laboratories and the development of a resident program of study next came into being. The GIA became a nonprofit organization in 1934 under a Board of Governors chosen from professionals from the jewelry industry, business, and research scientists, and the organization retains this structure today.

Over 40,000 persons -- jewelers, hobbyists, and others -- have studied with the GIA.

THE COURSES

The GIA offers many different courses. Our interest lies with the colored stones, gem identification, and diamond courses.

The GIA offers these courses in such a way as to make it easy for people who lead busy lives. They have both home study and resident courses. In some cases they recommend taking certain resident courses in conjunction with home study courses to gain the practical knowledge necessary to have access to needed gemological equipment. By offering a number of course options the GIA can provide equipment, pre-graded stones, and other necessities which contribute to successful completion of course work.

HOME STUDY COURSES

These courses are designed to be self-pacing. The average course takes about 26 weeks to complete, if a person were to schedule one evening a week to study. However, there is not a time limit and a student may work as fast or as slow as desired. Lessons are individually corrected and commented upon in writing by an assigned instructor. Any stones lent may be kept until lesson completion and the student has grasped fully the content of that lesson. Diplomas and /or certificates are awarded upon successful completion of all courses.

COLORED STONE COURSE

This course, a prerequisite to the Gem Identification Course, earns the student the Colored Stone Certificate when both are completed.

An introductory course, it includes the study of all colored gemstones (excluding diamonds), pearls and synthetics. The student receives an introduction to the world of gemstones, how they are different from minerals, and what makes them valuable. You are taught how to quickly recognize key properties of colored stones and what tests to use in identifying gems.

There are a total of 44 lessons, requiring no special equipment, and a supervised written examination of the material covered qualifies the student to take the Gem Identification Course.

GEM IDENTIFICATION COURSE

With so many imitation and synthetic stones appearing on the market, positive gem identification becomes very important. This course offers the student the opportunity to learn valuable skills through a series of identification projects and techniques. The GIA furnishes over 200 pre-graded stones for the student to practice these identifications.

The Gem Identification Course, consisting of 39 lessons, requires the student to either acquire or have access to a number of pieces of gemological equipment, which can be purchased as the student progresses through the course. The most important ones and on the "must" list are:

- refractometer
- polariscope
- a 10x corrected loupe
- specific gravity liquids
- dichroscope
- polarizing filter
- tweezer

Fortunately, these instruments can be used at either of the two GIA centers (if you live near them or take the resident courses concurrently) or purchased through GIA's subsidiary, Gem Instruments Corporation.

Some useful instruments, but not absolutely necessary, include a binocular microscope, ultraviolet light, thermal reaction tester, spectroscope, immersion cell, and emerald filter.

To pass this course the student must achieve 100% on a proctored stone examination.

THE DIAMOND COURSE

A wealth of information is taught in this course, not the least of which is the GIA's famous Diamond Grading System. In 43 lessons the student covers the following material:

- diamond clarity, color and cut
- evaluation of all sizes and shapes of loose and mounted diamonds
- buying, selling and keeping up with prices
- detection of treated and coated diamonds

- estimating diamond weight
- history of diamonds, genesis, mining, fashioning
- marketing structure

The lessons also include other useful information such as legal pitfalls, insurance safeguards, and establishing an appraisal service. The only equipment needed is a pair of tweezers and a 10x loupe.

After successful completion of a proctored written examination the Diamond Certificate is awarded.

RESIDENT COURSES

The GIA offers two resident courses: full-time resident training and mini-resident courses.

FULL-TIME RESIDENT TRAINING

This course requires that the student spend six months in resident training at either the Santa Monica, California, or New York City Facility. During this time the student has an opportunity to do work of a special laboratory nature with diamonds and colored stones. After successful completion, the student receives The Graduate Gemologist in Residence Diploma. Because of the specialized nature of this course, we suggest writing to the GIA for particulars. At the end of this chapter we have the address listed.

MINI-RESIDENT COURSES

Mini-resident classes are for one or two weeks either in Santa Monica, California, or New York and at other designated major cities throughout the United States. If the student elects to take one of the associated doorstep option programs held in cities across the United States, any instruments needed are made available. Otherwise, there may be some equipment needs which a student will have to provide if taking only the home study course. However, a student may rent equipment for a modest fee at either the Santa Monica, California, or New York locations. All students receive individual attention and assistance with their studies and enrollment is strictly limited to maintain this standard.

Being a student or graduate of GIA courses entitles you to free consultations on merchandising or professional problems you may encounter.

As mentioned before, the GIA recommends resident classes be taken concurrently with the home study courses. The two classes which are particularly useful are one-week courses in diamond grading and gem identification. These courses are offered both at Santa Monica, New York, and, by utilizing the Doorstep Program, in many cities throughout the United States.

DIAMOND GRADING

While teaching accurate techniques and procedures, this course covers the use of diamond instruments; clarity grading; color analysis and classification; proportion grading and finish analysis; weight estimation; and common diamond simulants.

GEM IDENTIFICATION

Four main areas are covered in this hands-on course -- key gem testing instruments use; gem identification techniques; recognizing synthetics; synthetic emeralds, rubies, alexandrities; plus some new stones just on the market.

After the student completes all of the above courses, and a final writing examination, a Graduate Gemologist Diploma (G.G.) is awarded. Please note, the GIA recommends students *start* with the Diamond Course if they are planning to earn this diploma. Do send for the GIA brochure and information which expands further on this information.

GEMMOLOGICAL* ASSOCIATION OF GREAT BRITAIN

This organization, founded in 1908 as the educational committee of the National Association of Goldsmiths, issues the highly scientific and well-known Fellowship Diploma of the Association also referred to as the FGA (Fellow Gemmological Association). In 1937 the Association reorganized as the Gemmological

*note: In Great Britain the word "gemmology" is spelled with two "m's".

Association, seeking incorporation as the Gemmological Association of Great Britain in 1947.

Like the the GIA, the Gemmological Association of Great Britain maintains a non-profit educational scientific status and numbers the following among its objectives:

- promotion of the study of gemology
- establishment of educational systems
- holding of examinations
- awarding diplomas, certificates, medals and scholarships
- maintaining libraries, laboratories and collections of gem materials
- scientific and industrial study of materials and articles pertinent to gemology

The Association has graduated some 3,500 people during the past 50 years.

THE COURSES

The Association offers unique correspondence courses annually from October through May, with examinations held in June. These courses are extremely popular and usually reach their capacity very quickly. Divided in two parts -- preliminary and diploma (1 year each) -- homework and papers are scheduled every two weeks. Students receive the personal guidance and supervision of an instructor, with all work being individually corrected and any problems receiving special attention.

While the Association allows students to study without taking the examination, 19 separate examination centers are maintained in major countries around the world, and the Association maintains affiliations with eight gemological institutes in other countries.

Because the content of each of these course sections is so comprehensive, we are only providing a brief outline. We recommend you send to the Association (see end of chapter for address) for a complete information packet.

THE PRELIMINARY COURSE -- FIRST YEAR

The following is a partial outline of the contents of this course, which is purely theoretical.

I. Elementary crystallography
II. Elementary physical and optical properties
   A. hardness, cleavage
   B. specific gravity
   C. the use of heavy liquids
   D. reflection, refraction, and polarization
   E. nature of color
III. Use of gem-testing equipment
IV. Description of gem materials
   A. color, chemical composition, crystal system, cleavage, hardness, etc., for the most popular gems
   B. synthetic and imitation stones
   C. organic products - pearls, amber, coral
V. Fashioning of gemstones

The Diploma Course -- Second Year

This course includes all of the content of the preliminary plus the following, which again is a partial outline.

THEORY:
I.   Elementary crystallography -- expanded
II.   Physical and optical properties
    A.   advanced techniques of preliminary course
    B.   spectroscopy and absorption spectra
    C.   luminescent and electrical properties
    D.   application of x-rays and ultraviolet light to gem testing
    E.   inclusions
III.   Apparatus: units of measurement
    A.   use of balance, microscope, polariscope, refractometer, dichroscope, spectroscope, and ultraviolet lamps
    B.   endoscope and table spectrometer
IV.   Description of gem materials
    A.   advanced identification: color, chemical composition, crystal system, cleavage hardness, etc., for the most popular gems
    B.   outstanding features of gem identification
    C.   synthetic and composite stones, glass and plastic imitations
    D.   organic products -- pearl, amber, coral
V.   Fashioning of gemstones -- diamond cutters and lapidaries

PRACTICAL:
Actual hands-on identification of the following properties of gemstones.

- refractive indices and birefringence
- dichroism
- specific gravity
- absorption spectra
- identification of cut/uncut and mounted/unmounted gemstones
- estimation of weight

In addition to all of the above, the Association provides a very comprehensive book list and suggestions for gathering other practical information, both theoretical and instrumentational.

It is important to point out that if the student expects to achieve success with these courses, he should have access to, or be prepared to buy, the necessary gemological equipment recommended by the Association.

SUMMARY

Once again, we want to emphasize the importance of education. However, we also realize that not everyone would have the time to spend studying all of these courses, in spite of the fact that they are valuable in their content. Also, because these courses are not specifically designed for the collector, as we pointed out earlier, no doubt a person would not want to take all of these courses. We recommend that, as a collector, you zero in on those courses which are in your area of interest.

Sources:

Gemmological Association of Great Britain
St. Dunstan's House
Carey Lane
London, E.C. 2V 8AB
England

Gemological Institute of America
1660 Stewart Street
P.O. Box 2110
Santa Monica, California 90406
310-829-2991

Gemological Institute of America
1180 Avenue of the Americas
New York, New York 10036
212-944-5900

KUNZITE CRYSTAL

This fine example of a natural spodumene crystal yielded two cut gems over 700 cts., one over 500 cts., and a final gem of over 150 cts. These gems were cut by author John Ramsey -- see photo of spodumene in the gem reference section.

RED TOPAZ

An extremely unusual, rare, and fine color Imperial topaz from the Ouro Preto mining district in Minas Gerais, Brazil.

SWISS BLUE TOPAZ

A good example of the electric blue color displayed in Swiss blue topaz. These pieces are cut in a double mirror design.

MOONSTONE

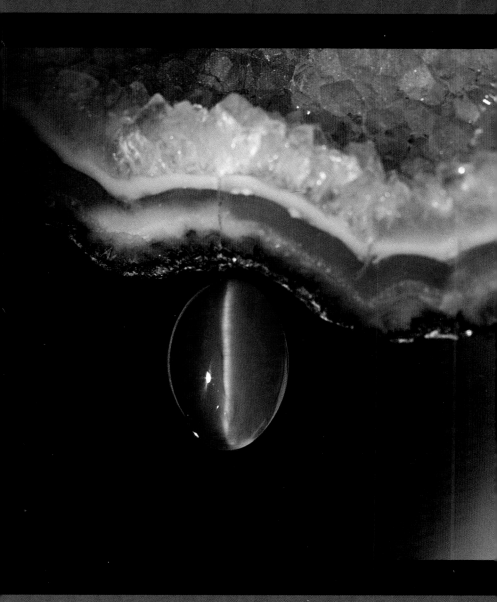

A well defined "eye" shows on this Indian moonstone. Normally the asterism associated with moonstone is less well defined.

GOLCONDA TOURMALINE MINE

A historically significant tourmaline mine in Minas Gerais, Brazil. According to the current owner the Golconda has produced tourmaline since the turn of the century. It boasts a production of indicolite, rubellite, and green tourmaline as well as industrial minerals.

GREEN BERYL

A rough crystal of green beryl can be transformed into an exceptional large faceted gem or a carved bust for the collector.

RED SPINEL, BURMA

This spinel from Burma is of exceptional quality. Notice the color saturation.

OURO PRETO, MINAS GERAIS, BRAZIL

This charming town dating from Portuguese imperial times is famous for its Imperial topaz and for its many majestic churches and cobblestone streets.

FLUORITE

The cut of this stone was designed by the author. This New Hampshire fluorite weighs over 300 carats.

COLOMBO, SRI LANKA

Friend of the authors, this young snake charmer demonstrates his art.

LONDON BLUE TOPAZ

Large, brightly faceted London blue topaz, with a topaz crystal specimen and an antique miner's lamp.

THE CAPAO IMPERIAL TOPAZ MINE

Working long hours these garimpeiros (miners) dig for Imperial topaz. The earth seems to mirror the color of the imperial topaz it yields.

RUBELLITE TOURMALINE

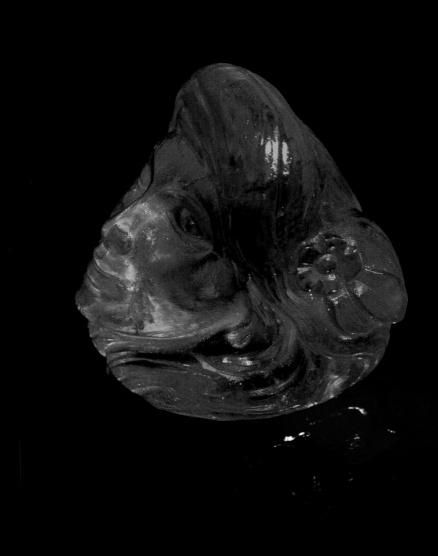

Masterfully carved female bust of rubellite tourmaline. The work was done in Idar-Oberstein where lapidary has been an art for centuries.

BRAZILIAN AQUAMARINE

This 76 carat aquamarine brooch with diamond chevrons was designed by Laura Ramsey -- aquamarine has graced fine jewelry for centuries.

AUSTRALIAN OPAL

This opal and diamond ring in 18kt gold was designed by co-author Laura Ramsey. Lightening Ridge, New South Wales, Australia produces some of the worlds finest opal.

PEARL

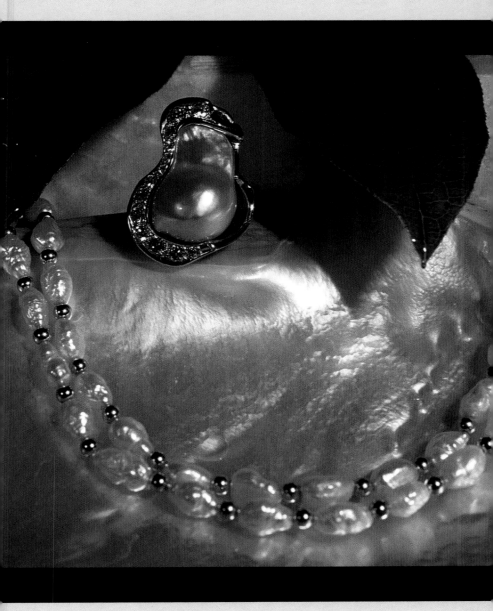

A timeless classic--gold, diamond, and pearl jewelry. Natures treasures combined.

IMPERIAL TOPAZ CRYSTAL PENDANT

Pendant fashioned from a bi-colored Imperial topaz crystal. The dual color phenomenon shown here is unusual in Imperial topaz.

DEMANTOID GARNET CRYSTAL

This fine crystal of demantoid garnet is from Italy. A most rare gem, this particular crystal is mentioned in the Italian Dictionary of Mineralogy and once belonged to the author and his father.

IN SEARCH OF TOURMALINE

Laura Ramsey visits a Brazilian tourmaline mine. Blasted out of hard rock, any tourmaline from this mine is worth virtually any price asked.

INDICOLITE TOURMALINE

An indicolite tourmaline and diamond ring for that special someone. The blue color in tourmaline is rare and coveted.

AFRICAN TREASURES

Two newcomers to the world of gems, both tanzanite and tsavorite capture the lead in popular gemstones. East Africa boasts a rich resource in these beautiful gems.

INDICOLITE TOURMALINE

This 14 carat deep blue indicolite tourmaline is a fine example of collectible quality tourmaline. Rare both in color and size, this blue tourmaline is from Brazil.

PINK TOPAZ

An unusual color variety of topaz, pink topaz comes primarily from Brazil and Pakistan. This cushion cut gem is surrounded by diamonds and set in white gold.

AFRICAN AMETHYST

Selections of jewelry designs by co-author Laura Ramsey in deep rich African amethyst.

FELDSPAR, PLUSH OREGON

The popular name for this type of feldspar is "Sunstone". Sunstone is the state gem of Oregon. The stone in this ring has exceptional red color and is surrounded with the rough material.

KING TUTANKHAMEN

Morganite bust of King Tutankhamen carved by master carvers in Idar-Oberstein, Germany.

IV

DIAMONDS

DIAMOND SOURCES

There used to be only one criterion widely used to grade diamonds for their value, their weight, measured in carats. As the diamond trade grew and became more valuable other factors became important to refine the value of an individual stone. The other factors used in grading diamonds nowadays are cut, clarity, and color. We will explain these factors to you and as you become more knowledgeable about diamonds you will be better able to judge their value for yourself. We will also explain about the certification of diamonds and how this certificate is relied on by buyer and seller to accurately reflect the value of a stone.

Diamonds were discovered in Africa in 1867, the first being a 21 ½ carat pebble which appealed to a child playing alongside a river. The stone was then given to a neighbor, Schalk van Niekirk, who had admired it. The stone was later appraised in Grahamstown and the appraiser confirmed that the pebble was a diamond. Van Niekirk continued his quest for diamonds and in 1869 bought the 83 ½ carat Star of South Africa from a native African for 500 sheep, 10 oxen, and a horse. He later sold the diamond in Hopetown for £11,200. This started the

the diamond in Hopetown for £11,200. This started the diamond rush in earnest and led to the discovery of many alluvial deposits within the next few years.

The technology of diamond recovery in alluvial deposits is such that the first mining of the deposit effectively recovers most of the diamonds; any reworking of the deposit is not cost-effective. Because of this, alluvial deposits usually pan out very quickly unless the claim is worked methodically by only one company. Hard rock diamond mines usually have richer deposits and are worked for a much longer period of time. Diamond mines are known as "pipes" because the mines are the lava channels of extinct volcanoes which died out a very long time ago. It is believed that diamonds were formed at a depth of around 240 miles and were carried to the surface by volcanic activity.

The Jagersfontein mine was discovered in 1870 by the foreman of the Jagersfontein farm, located near the town of Fauresmith, South Africa. The mine continued to produce until 1971. In 1871 the DeBeers mine was discovered on the Vooruitzigt farm near Kimberley, South Africa. DeBeers Consolidated Mines, Ltd. owns this mine as well as four others within a few miles. These mines are the Dutoitspan, Bultfontein, Kimberley, and Wesselton. These are known as the "Big Five" or as the DeBeers Mines.

There are over a hundred mines in South Africa and one of the most important is the Premier Mine which was discovered in 1903 in the Transvaal. The 3106 carat Cullinan, the largest diamond ever found, was mined from the Premier in 1905. Two famous alluvial diamonds, the 726 carat Jonker and the 287 carat Pohl, were discovered nearby in 1934. Other diamond producing countries in

Diamond Nomenclature

Brilliants >0.47ct.	GIA	IDC	CIBJO
Color	D E F G H I→J K→L M→Z Fancy diamonds	Exceptional white + Exceptional white Rare white + Rare white White Slightly tinted white Tinted white Tinted Color 1 Tinted Color 2 Tinted Color 3 Tinted Color 4	Exceptional white + Exceptional white Rare white + Rare white White Slightly tinted white Tinted White Tinted Color Fancy Diamonds
Clarity	Flawless Internally flawless Very, very slightly VVS 1 & 2 included Very slightly included VS 1 & 2 Slightly included Imperfect SI 1 & 2 I 1, 2 & 3	Loupe Clean VVS 1 & 2 VS 1 & 2 SI P 1, 2 & 3	 Loupe Clean VVS 1 & 2 VS 1 & 2 SI P I, II & II
	10x Loupe. External faults influence the clarity grade	10x Loupe. Except for "loupe clean" all faults affect the clarity grade.	10x Loupe. External faults are not evaluated unless their removal entails considerable weight loss.
Cut	Proportions: No evaluation American Ideal Cut is the basis. Finish (symmetry & polish): very good, good, medium and poor.	Proportions: Cut is evaluated as good, medium, or poor. Finish: very good, good, medium, and poor.	Proportions: No evaluation, poor cut is mentioned under remarks. Finish: very good, good, medium, and poor.

Table 1 Various Grading Systems

Africa are Zimbabwe, Sierra Leone, Ivory Coast, Gabon, Tanzania, Liberia, and Botswana.

The basis of any diamond grading is a nomenclature. These are widely understood rules for the description of the various quality features of diamonds. A nomenclature, for the most part, has its origin in present-day trade practices. Some of the important nomenclatures are:

- GIA - Gemological Institute of America. The GIA is a non-profit educational institution of the jewelry industry. The GIA conducts courses in gemology and runs trade laboratories as well. In both instances a grading system was needed. The nomenclature of the GIA grading system is currently the world standard.

- CIBJO - Confédération Internationale de la Bijouterie, Joaillerie, Orfèvrerie, des Diamants, Perles et Pierres, an international association of the jewelry, silver, pearl, and stone trades, founded in 1961.

- IDC - International Diamond Council, a joint committee set up by the CIBJO, WFDB (World Federation of Diamond Bourses), and the IDMA (International Diamond Manufacturers Association) to work out a consistent set of rules for diamond trading which would be valid throughout the world.

Table 1 shows a comparison of the different nomenclatures. We will focus almost exclusively on the GIA nomenclature as it is the most widely used system in the United States. The GIA first developed a system of diamond grading in the middle thirties.

COLOR

The color of a gemstone is one of its most important characteristics and one of the most noticeable to human eyes. The color range in diamonds is extensive; it varies from pink through red, blue, green, yellow, brown, and even black! The colors are caused by trace amounts of other elements which have been incorporated into the carbon lattice of the diamond. The blue color is caused by about 1 aluminum atom for every 20 million carbon atoms. Pink diamonds are caused by manganese, yellow by nitrogen. The rarest color for a diamond is red, followed by green, blue, purple, and brown. While the rarest diamond is red, it is colorless diamonds which are the basis of the diamond trade. Diamonds are the only gemstones where no color is highly prized.

The color terms used to be based on the source where these colors were most commonly found. Some of these terms were Jager, River, Wesselton, Cape, and Premier. "Jager" referred to the Jagersfontein Mine. Many of these stones were faintly blue in color, mostly due to strong fluorescence. Diamonds that were found in river or alluvial deposits were believed to be of slightly better quality than diamonds found in pipe mines.

GIA COLOR TABLE

GIA Grades	Traditional Terms	Descriptive Terms	General Terms (<0.47 ct.)
D	River	Rarest White	
E			White
F	Top	Rare	White
G	Wesselton	White	
H	Wesselton	White	
I	Top Crystal	Slightly Tinted	Slightly Tinted
J	Crystal	White	White
K	Top	Tinted	Tinted
L	Cape	White	White
M	Cape	Slightly	
N		Yellowish	
O			Tinted Color
P	Light	Yellowish	
Q	Yellow		
R			
S-Z	Yellow	Yellow	

Table 2

The Wesselton Mine produced one color grade that was better than the top grade found in many of the other pipes, so "Wesselton" can be applied to any very slightly tinted stone. "Cape" referred to Cape of Good Hope, or South Africa. Since these stones were distinctly more yellow than their Brazilian counterparts, "Cape" became the accepted term for strongly yellow tinted diamonds. The Premier Mine produced a significant proportion of diamonds with a pronounced yellow cast which fluoresced a strong blue in daylight. The result is an oily body color that came to be associated with the Premier pipe. Premiers are often called "Coal-Oil Blue" for this reason.

Today, these are known as the "old terms" and their use has been replaced by a letter series. The best color quality is known as "River" and is designated today by the letter D. Colored diamonds are called "fancy diamonds" and are designated by the letter Z.

COLOR GRADING

The color of a diamond is graded by comparing it to a set of master stones which have been certified by the appropriate organization. These certified stones grade out at the lower boundary of their color grade so that the consumer is assured the color of the tested diamond is better than or equal to the master stone. Since a larger diamond transmits proportionately more light than a smaller one, it is much easier to accurately classify a large stone. For this reason, the color scale is weighted, becoming less restrictive as the diamond becomes smaller.

WEIGHTED COLOR SCALE

Color Grade	≤ 0.20 ct.	0.20 ↔ 0.60 ct.	0.60 ↔ 1.50 ct.	≥ 1.50 ct.
Exceptional White	Colorless	Colorless	Colorless	Colorless
Rare White				
White				
Slightly Tinted White	Slight trace of color	Slight trace of color	Slight trace of color	Slight trace of color
Tinted White				
Tinted	Clear trace of color	Clear trace of color	Clear trace of color	Clear trace of color
			Perceptible color	Perceptible color

Table 3

CLARITY

Flawless, *
Internally flawless
Loupe Clean (<.47 ct.)

Flawless: Cut diamond free from internal and external flaws using a 10 power microscope.
Internally Flawless: Cut diamond absolutely free from internal faults using a 10 power microscope. External features should be so small that they can easily be removed by polishing the stone.

VVS 1 & 2

VVS 1 (10x Loupe) No inclusions in the field of the table. Very, very small inclusions are allowed in the rest of the stone. Minimal external faults.
VVS 2 (10x Loupe) Very, very small inclusions anywhere in the stone. Only very small external defects allowed.

SI 1 & 2

SI 1 (10x Loupe) Small faults internally or under the table, not visible to the naked eye. Some definite external features.
SI 2 (10x Loupe) Small, easily discernible inclusions in the table, not visible to the naked eye. Some definite external features.

I 1, 2, & 3

P 1 (10x Loupe and naked eye) Inclusion easily recognizable with the loupe, difficult to see with the naked eye through the crown, does not influence the brilliance. Definite external faults.
P 2 (10x Loupe and naked eye) Large and numerous inclusions, just visible with the naked eye through the crown. Diminishes the brilliance. Definite external faults.
P 3 (naked eye) Large and numerous inclusions, easily visible with the naked eye. Diminishes the brilliance. Definite external faults.

The term clarity refers to the number and size of inclusions present in the cut diamond. These inclusions were formed because of the mineral impurities or varying conditions present during the diamond's formation. The mineral impurities most commonly found are red garnet, brown spinel, green enstatite and diopside, and dark brown or black ilmenite, magnetite, and graphite. Pressures and temperatures which vary during the formation of diamonds can also cause internal flaws. These flaws are often fracture, tension, or cleavage cracks.

All diamonds have inlcusions. It is only a matter of the magnification required to make them visible. For this reason, the GIA and other international diamond standards organizations have standardized their grading using a 10x loupe. The GIA grades for clarity are flawless, internally flawless, very very slightly included (VVS 1 & 2), very slightly included (VS1 & VS2), slightly included (S1 & S2), and imperfect (I1, I2, & I3).

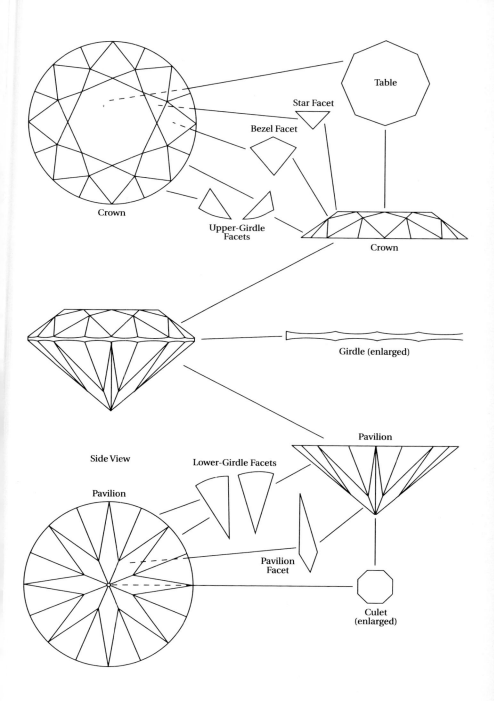

**Figure 1   Facets of a Diamond:
Standard Round Brilliant**

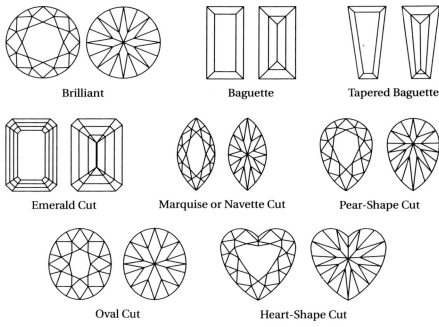

Brilliant Baguette Tapered Baguette

Emerald Cut Marquise or Navette Cut Pear-Shape Cut

Oval Cut Heart-Shape Cut

Figure 2 Sample Cuts

As you can see, diamonds can be and are cut into many shapes such as pears, baguettes, marquise, emerald-cut, heart-shaped, square-cut, and many others. The "classic" cut, however, is the round brilliant with at least 32 facets and a table on the crown, and at least 24 facets and a culet on the pavilion. The brilliant cut dates back to the first century B.C, but did not gain popularity until the middle of the 17th century. In the early twentieth century, the necessary proportions to produce the most brilliance were empirically and theoretically derived. The brilliance of a diamond is made up of many components.

These components are:

External Brilliance   Light reflection off the facet surfaces, also known as "luster".

Internal Brilliance   Refraction and reflection of light on the pavilion facets.

Dispersive Brilliance   The splitting of light into its component colors, also known as "fire".

Scintillation Brilliance   Reflections of the light source by the diamond.

Very small brilliants, 1 or 2 points in size, often appear lifeless and milky, since the light reflections off of 57 tiny facets can no longer be resolved by the human eye. If very small stones are cut differently to reduce the number of facets they may look more brilliant and transparent. Conversely, many of the large and famous diamonds of the world have been re-cut to increase their number of facets and their brilliance.

DIAMONDS:
QUESTIONS & ANSWERS

WHAT ABOUT LAWS DEALING WITH DIAMONDS?

The Federal Trade Commission defines a diamond as follows: "A natural mineral consisting essentially of pure carbon, crystallized in the cubic system and found in many colors. Its hardness is 10 on the Mohs scale, its specific gravity approximately 3.52, and it has a refractive index of 2.417." Anything not meeting this definition, and not symmetrically fashioned with at least seventeen polished facets, cannot be advertised or sold as a diamond. If the stone meets the definition, but does not have seventeen polished facets, it must be called a rough or unpolished diamond, whichever applies. An imitation or simulated diamond must be clearly designated as such.

WHAT ABOUT APPRAISALS -- THEY SEEM SO CONFUSING?

Correct terminology used in describing diamonds often creates an appraisal problem by generating confusion among insurance companies, estate sellers, banks and owners of stones. An individual sold a stone as perfect often feels the appraisal value should be higher than quoted and is often upset, according to some jewelers. It is possible for one man to appraise a ring at $800 and another at $1200; both jewelers can be honest and both are appraising at simply what they regard as the true market value of the diamond. Actually, there is not one chance in a thousand that a diamond taken to six different stores will be given the same appraisal by any two of them.

HOW DOES THE FTC PROTECT THE CUSTOMER?

1. The Federal Trade Commission rulings specify that all weight representations of diamonds shall be subject to a one-half point tolerance.
2. The weight of all diamonds in a ring must be qualified to indicate that the figure given represents the total weight.
3. That diamond imitations cannot be referred to as gems, reproductions or replicas.
4. That it is unfair trade practice to sell artificially colored diamonds without stating that they are so colored.

WHAT IS A CERTIFICATE?

This is a report accompanying a diamond attesting to its quality, carat weight, clarity grade, color grade and cutting.

SHOULD A DIAMOND BE REMOVED FROM THE MOUNTING FOR AN APPRAISAL?

No, not unless there is an extremely important reason for this to be done. Too many things can happen to it, it can be lost, strayed, stolen or broken.

HOW MUCH SHOULD A GEM APPRAISAL COST?

This is based on the time and cost of making the appraisal.

HOW OFTEN SHOULD A DIAMOND BE APPRAISED?

At least every one to three years, due to the appreciation potential.

CAN A DIAMOND'S COLOR BE CHANGED BY CUTTING AND POLISHING?

To a reasonable degree the original rough crystal can be altered. There are times when the original crystal's color should be preserved. When this is the situation, the diamond is fashioned so that it is heavier in appearance. But if the rough crystal has an undesirable color, the diamond is made as thin as possible without fully sacrificing the proper angles for dispersion and brilliance.

HOW IS COLOR CHECKED?

Most jewelers have three to eight small diamonds (usually third carat stones) that have been carefully checked for color and these are used as comparison stones. When a diamond is checked against these, the grade of whiteness can be determined.

WHAT IS THE MOST EFFECTIVE LIGHT SOURCE FOR COLOR GRADING?

By using a specialized diamond light of constant source. Daylight, because of its ultraviolet content and because it is not constant from day to day, nor constant from one locality to another, is not the most efficient.

WHAT IS MEANT BY MASTER DIAMONDS?

Experience has shown that the color of diamonds can be determined more objectively and more certainly by direct comparison with specially graded diamonds. For comparisons, a set of master diamonds in the stages from D to Z is used, whose exact values have previously and objectively been measured by the photometer or similar instrument.

WHAT IS MEANT BY INCLUSIONS?

These are internal fractures such as cleavages, cracks, fractures, tension cracks, feathers, structural defects, crystal inclusions, twinning planes or twin lines. Cleavages are cracks which run in the direction of planes of atoms. Fractures are cracks in any other direction not in a cleavage plane. Tension cracks usually surround a crystal inclusion and originate through the differential in thermal expansion of the enclosed foreign material. Crystal inclusions are minerals, which according to their nature, may be colorless, or red, brown, yellow or black. Feathers are fractures, cleavages or tension cracks which when observed at right angles to the crack plane look white and feather-like. Structural defects may be clouds or obscurities, these are microscopic crystals which appear like dust. Twin planes or twinning lines occur usually as fine, curved lines which cross the pavilion facets.

WHAT IS THE PURPOSE OF AN INDEPENDENT GEMOLOGICAL LABORATORY?

A gem lab should be an independent entity that neither buys or sells the diamonds it certifies. Acceptable terminology for diamond grading in the United States are standards established by the GIA. All lab personnel should be GIA graduates with applicable degrees and experience in grading.

WILL DIAMOND GRADES BE CONSISTENT FROM ALL LABORATORIES?

Diamond grading is not an exact science and subjective opinions differ slightly. However, differences in high color and clarity grades are less tolerated because the standards are more precise, i.e. if a diamond receives a grade of "Flawless", it cannot contain any inclusions visible under proper magnification and lighting. The same rules apply in the break between the "SI" grades and the "I" grades. In cases of small discrepancies, the buyer and seller should be able to reach a compromise through a well defined exchange program.

IF I PURCHASE A DIAMOND AND TAKE IT TO MY LOCAL JEWELER, WHAT IF I AM TOLD THAT I PAID TOO MUCH?

Because of potential profit, this situation occurs all too often. To get a better idea of your recently acquired diamonds, it is better to describe the carat weight, color and clarity to your jeweler and ask what it would cost to duplicate that exact item. This technique will give you a far more accurate idea of value at a retail level. This is especially true if you demand a stone that has been graded by an independent lab.

HOW DO I KNOW IF THE CERTIFICATION MATCHES MY DIAMOND?

Since the millimeter measurements are carried out to 1/100 of a decimal place, this information along with clarity, color and plot will serve to match the stone. In the event of any discrepancy, this stone and certificate may be returned to the lab for re-verification.

WHAT ARE THE KEY FACTORS TO LOOK FOR ON THE DIAMOND CERTIFICATE?

Other than the carat weight, clarity grade, color grade and cutting proportions, any diamond over 0.50 carats (1/2 carat) should contain a top and bottom plot or diagram of all internal and external inclusions. This drawing further serves to re-identify your diamond if you decide to have it set in jewelry.

WHAT DOES MELEE MEAN?

The word "melee" comes from the French word meaning a confused mass. It is used collectively to describe small, round diamonds with full or single cuts when sold or shown in lots. The term refers to diamonds up to 29 points. Because labor is a very large factor in the total cost of melee, it is more economical to cut these stones overseas.

WHAT ABOUT CERTIFICATES ON SMALL DIAMONDS OR MELEE?

Should you purchase a parcel of small stones, it is still necessary to have a certificate. The document will not contain a plot for each stone, but should have individual carat weight, measurements, clarity and color ranges as follows:

Clarity	Color
IF to VVS	D to F
VS	G to H
SI1	I to J
SI2	K to L
I	M to N

The above format will guarantee your purchase. It is important to note that the Gem Trade Lab of the

Gemological Institute of America does not currently offer a certification on a diamond smaller than 0.23 carats.

IS IT POSSIBLE TO GRADE DIAMONDS THAT ARE SET IN JEWELRY?

It is impossible to grade mounted diamonds accurately because the setting and any surrounding stones affect the color and also because one often has to look at the table where spectrum colors can confuse the eye. For insurance purposes, however, both ranges of clarity and color can be given to insure the jewelry for replacement purposes.

CAN INCLUSIONS EVER BE REMOVED?

If the inclusions are on or close to the surface, they can be polished off by slight recutting and refinishing. If the inclusion is deep inside the stone, it may sometimes be feasible to minimize or lighten it through the use of a laser beam.

WHAT EXACTLY DOES LASER DRILLING DO TO A DIAMOND?

A very small hole is drilled down to the inclusion with laser beam and then acid is introduced down the hole to decolor the inclusion.

IS THE HOLE LEFT BY THE DRILLING VISIBLE TO THE UNAIDED EYE?

No. This laser channel is only five-thousandths of an inch in diameter.

DOES LASER DRILLING AFFECT THE VALUE OF THE DIAMOND?

In many cases the clarity grade of a particular stone may be upgraded, primarily due to the fact that a light or whitish inclusion is far less obvious that the black or dark inclusion which existed prior to the laser drilling.

Conversion Chart for Round Diamonds -- Carats to Millimeters

CTS	MM	CTS	MM
.005	1.0	.18	3.7
.0075	1.2	.20	3.8
.01	1.3	.22	3.9
.015	1.5	.23	4.0
.02	1.7	.25	4.1
.25	1.8	.30	4.2
.03	2.0	.33	4.4
.035	2.1	.35	4.5
.04	2.2	.38	4.6
.05	2.4	.40	4.8
.06	2.5	.43	4.9
.07	2.7	.47	5.0
.08	2.8	.50	5.2
.09	2.9	.60	5.4
.10	3.3	.63	5.5
.11	3.1	.65	5.6
.12	3.2	.75	5.8
.14	3.3	.80	6.0
.15	3.4	.85	6.2
.16	3.5	.95	6.4
.17	3.6	1.00	6.5

V

APPRAISALS

WHAT'S BEEN GOING ON

In the appraisal arena there are three participants: the owner of the gem, the appraiser, and the gem itself. Of the three participants, only the gem has a constant and unvarying nature; its identity, clarity, color and carat weight are all objective facts. However, with respect to the other two participants, the gem owner and the appraiser, there are facts which may vary, that are not objective or easily detectable, but which are quite relevant to the subject matter of appraisals.

A device which will enable us to understand events in the appraisal scene will be to observe them from both the viewpoint of the appraisal customer and the viewpoint of the appraiser. This technique will show that what may appear to be a simple and straightforward service can be a much more complex issue than ever imagined. For the collector, learning about appraisals is much like walking into a movie that is half over; a great deal of explaining must be done in order to know what has been happening.

WHAT IS AN APPRAISAL:

THE CUSTOMER'S VIEW

From the standpoint of the appraisal customer, there is a great deal of variance in the conception of what constitutes an appraisal. Appraisal customers approach the appraisal process with a wide range of experience, exposure and knowledge. Due to the differences brought to the appraisal process by the customer, no general public concept defining an appraisal has developed. Perhaps if a poll were taken asking: "What is an appraisal?", the common answer would be "An appraisal is taking a gem to your local jeweler to find out what it is worth." Underlying such a statement are several assumptions which bear examination.

One such assumption, also itself dependent upon many factors, is validity. When an appraisal customer wants to "find out what a gem is worth," he assumes the assigned value will be valid. Perhaps one of the reasons for assuming validity can be found in the perception-set of our overall economy. With many items we buy the assumption that, they are what they pretend to be, is justified. After all, at the grocery store, one can of green beans usually can be thought to be somewhat similar to another. At an automobile dealership, it is relatively correct to assume that, for a given make and model, there will be little difference from one dealership to another. Because we are accustomed to assembly line products which have assembly line predictability and uniformity, this idea cannot help but unconsciously mislead us in other areas to which this notion does not apply. We therefore take it for granted that an appraisal . . . is an appraisal . . . is an appraisal.

The fact that each appraiser is in effect his own factory, making each appraisal by hand, makes it logical to expect a certain lack of uniformity. Appraisals are not assembly line products. Each appraisal receives individual, handmade attention, which is really what customers and collectors want and expect.

The individual, handmade aspect of all appraisals, and resulting lack of uniformity, calls into question the relative validity of one appraisal versus another. In areas where people are accustomed to handmade products, such as their barber or hairdresser, people tend to be very particular and weed out the undesirable practitioners. They also expect a lack of uniformity. Familiarity with a subject gives a basis for choice and we do tend to get more haircuts than appraisals. However, in beginning to understand the nature of appraisals, the realization awakens that perhaps there might be a certain lack of uniformity in appraisals.

Another aspect of the assumption of "validity" can be found in the word "official". Similar to our assumption of assembly line uniformity, an assumption exists that a product complies to official standards of some kind. Many items or services for sale require official standards in composition or official requirement for the people offering the service. Composition standards exist in the food we eat (enriched flour); the cars we drive (safety standards); and the houses we buy (building standards). In addition to composition standards, there are professional standards -- lawyers, doctors, pilots, truck drivers -- almost any profession has legally imposed official standards for the person providing the service. The net result, psychologically, means the customer believes he has received a legal blessing from the word "official."

Again, as with assembly line uniformity, officialism assumes a very pervasive place in our society; so pervasive that it may be assumed to exist when it does not. The fact is, however, that anyone can give a gemstone appraisal and charge money for it. There are no *official* standards.

WHAT'S IT WORTH?

Even if the problems of uniformity and officialism did not exist, and the validity of the appraisal were not in question, there still are several questions we must address. In our hypothetical definition of an appraisal we have been examining the part where the customer wants to "find out what it's worth." The part of that statement which deserves attention is the word *worth*. When asking the appraised worth of a gem the customer may not realize the complexity of that question. Each customer can and does have different and particular reasons for wanting to know the worth of his stone. Each person obtaining an appraisal might be attaching a different significance to the number of dollars which are equated to worth. The appraisal value can mean one of several things: retail price of the particular gem; replacement price of a similar stone in case of loss; the price at which the customer should be willing to sell to their private parties; the price at which the gem could be traded for land, cars, or yachts. There are any number of possible ideas which may be either consciously or unconsciously involved -- separately or combined.

WHY HAVE AN APPRAISAL?

If it is true that the general public has a fuzzy notion of what an appraisal is, we can also say the motives behind getting appraisals may not be clear cut either. We have already seen quite a few variables put into the appraisal equation by the customer, and the subject of motives brings more tangles to the fore.

We can put motives behind obtaining an appraisal into two categories: (1) To obtain the knowledge of what the appraisal says; (2) To act on the knowledge once obtained.

Although in the minority, there are a group of appraisal customers who obtain appraisals solely for the knowledge. A person inheriting Aunt What's-Her-Name's antique brooch might want to know whether its worth $10 or $10,000. Did his aunt really like him or was she playing one last joke? The same type of motive may also come from the recipient of a gift. A slightly different type of motive would come from someone who purchased an item. Someone may have purchased a gem at a garage sale, swap meet or auction without the slightest idea of worth and want to know if they did well. Similarly, a person buying a gem may be interested in obtaining a third-party opinion of the purchase. Then, too, it is not uncommon for a person to own a gem for a long period of time and simply be curious as to its current value.

The larger group of people and number of motives are found in the second category: those people who obtain an appraisal with the idea of acting on the information received. For example, a person inheriting an antique brooch might want to know if the gem's value means it should be placed in a safe deposit box. Resale is another motive. An owner may want to know whether a gem can be turned into cash if need arises, and how much cash.

An additional motivation which causes a person to act is fear of loss. The standard practice of insurance companies is to require an appraisal for any valuable items they insure. This is natural for several reasons. After all, if insurance companies did not demand appraisals, they could easily end up insuring worthless items for a large sum. An insurance appraisal helps give a clear understanding and an exact description of the insured item. The insurance appraisal also helps the insured in the event a replacement has to be obtained. When replacing a gem the more accurate the appraisal, the more satisfactory the claim resolution for the owner.

Another type of appraisal connected with insurance involves appraising the replacement gem. Assuming the insured is not an expert in the gemstone field he may want verification that the replacement gem has a value comparable to the lost stone, and not take the adjuster's word for it. From the standpoint of the consumer self-protection an accurate appraisal would be very helpful in evaluating an insurance replacement.

Another group which gets appraisals with action in mind are those who get them to show to family or friends. The motive, to obtain approval, also can change people buying solely for fun to the most purposeful of collectors. Gems seldom come cheap and understandably we seek positive reinforcement when spending large sums of money, especially to prove to one's family or peers the expenditures were worthwhile.

Resale is another important motive for obtaining an appraisal. Private parties are not alone in this regard because dealers use appraisals in marketing. Appraisals done by a competent appraiser can be invaluable to the person wishing to liquidate a gemstone. For resale it can be worth obtaining more than one appraisal -- especially if the dollars involved warrant the expense. Resale is a very reasonable motivation for obtaining an up-to-date appraisal. Appraisals which are too old tend to be discounted in their validity. Buying something costing a great deal of money from a private-party stranger, at best, can be an unnerving experience. Private parties who are selling do well to have the transaction as well prepared as possible and an up-to-date appraisal becomes a part of that preparedness. Such preparedness helps put everyone at ease and gives a reasonable basis for the transaction price.

APPRAISALS FROM THE APPRAISER'S VIEWPOINT

If the various psychological factors from the customer's side of appraisals seems complex, those on the side of the appraiser are at least their equal. Key factors involved in giving out appraisal information include: the appraiser's knowledge, willingness to act as a truly disinterested third party, and willingness to maintain a high quality product.

GEMOLOGICAL KNOWLEDGE

Knowledge in the appraisal field falls into two groups: gemological and commercial. Gemological knowledge consists of being able to correctly identify and, in the case of diamonds, grade the stones in question. Gemological expertise may be acquired in many different ways. Some of these ways are to study with the Gemological Institute of America, to study through the Gemological Association of Great Britain, or to learn through practical experience.

Correct identification involves the proper use of gemological equipment and a brief introduction here might be helpful. The four most basic pieces of equipment are: the refractometer, used to determine the refractive index of a stone; the polariscope which provides information on whether the stone is singly or doubly refractive; the microscope used to look for characteristic inclusions and to assess the quantity of inclusions; and finally, heavy liquids, which help in determining the specific gravity of a gem. Use of instruments becomes necessary for *proof* of identification. Any appraiser who says sight ID is enough should be regarded as unprofessional. In the case of diamonds, a color comparison set is an essential part of the gemological equipment. Anyone claiming the ability to accurately color grade diamonds without a comparison set should not be given credibility.

COMMERCIAL KNOWLEDGE

Commercial knowledge involves the ability to assign the proper value to the stones in question. For appraisal purposes an appraiser's gemological knowledge must be used in concert with a good knowledge of current market prices. Alone gemological knowledge is worthless.

Unfortunately, the acquisition of commercial knowledge can be the source of dilemma. In the past most appraisers were people also in the trade but the current trend has been toward appraisers who do not trade in gemstones. This raises two opposing arguments: how can a person know prices if he does not trade in gems and earn his living by that accurate knowledge; and, how can a person be a truly unbiased third party if he engages in trading in gems? Regardless of the dilemma, pricing stands out as the single most difficult area of knowledge to master in the gemstone field; particularly pricing in the colored stone market. This difficulty in pricing accounts for wholesalers specializing in certain gem varieties, i.e., aquamarine, topaz, jade, opal, rubies, or sapphires. However, just as a dealer can obtain an accurate knowledge of pricing in many areas, so can an appraiser.

THE DISINTERESTED THIRD PARTY

Any appraiser, even one without apparent reasons, can be induced away from his fiduciary responsibility to remain unbiased. However, two of the most time-honored inducements are what we call "punitive appraisals" and the "veiled offer to sell."

Punitive appraisals occur when an appraiser deliberately assigns a value to a gem lower than the true market value. We call this "punitive" because it occurs when the appraiser gives the low value to punish either the appraisal customer or the original vendor of the gem. First, deliberately low appraisals punish the appraisal customer by making him fear he has been taken advantage of by his supplier and, second, it punishes the original supplier as well by making that person look overly greedy and/or dishonest.

There can be several motivations for performing punitive appraisals, the most obvious being outrage that the appraiser missed the sale. The second involves awareness on the part of the appraiser that the customer lives in his area and he wants to have the customer for his own. The appraiser reasons, if the customer lives in his area, and as a gemstone buyer loses faith in his gem supplier, the customer will buy from the appraiser in the future. The lowball appraisal implies the gem would be cheaper if obtained from the appraiser. The error in the appraiser's line of reasoning lies in the fact that his actions harm everybody in the transaction, including himself. The customer loses faith not only in the person he bought from but also in the entire gemstone industry. Unfortunately, punitive appraisals are not at all uncommon.

THE VEILED OFFER TO SELL

The veiled offer to sell has a more complex structure than the punitive appraisal, based on there being a true offer to sell or a simple lack of communication, which only the participants know for sure. The veiled offer occurs when the appraiser believes the customer asks how much a gem is worth only to be followed by offering the gem to the appraiser for the amount stated. In some instances a person wants to sell a gem and lets the appraiser know only indirectly. This type of occurrence can only happen when there are ambiguities in the communication between the customer and the appraiser. However, this situation could never occur if the appraiser refuses to put himself in the position of being both buyer and appraiser. If the appraiser does not put himself in a neutral position there can be little room for objectivity.

WILLINGNESS TO MAINTAIN A HIGH QUALITY PRODUCT

Although an appraiser must have adequate knowledge and equipment and a willingness to act as a disinterested third party, he must also be willing to spend adequate time appraising a given stone. We call this third key factor in giving out appraisal information, in some ways less measurable than the other two, the willingness to maintain a high quality product or pride of workmanship.

A stone that looks like a spessartite garnet or Tanzanian grossular may just be one of the relatively unknown orange tourmalines from Kenya faceted in such a way as to hide its dichroism. Such a mis-identification could easily happen if an appraiser simply looked at a stone and made an assumption. Thorough procedure is important and flippancy never an adequate substitute for good, sound methods. All the proper gemological equipment, all the gemological and commercial knowledge, all the willingness to be a truly disinterested third party -- in fact, all of the ingredients discussed and a few not discussed -- are not enough if not well applied.

101

THE "FREEBIE" APPRAISAL

A notable and common occurrence familiar mostly to retailers we label the "freebie" appraisal. We want to discuss this type of appraisal based on two points: as common occurrence "freebies" affect the entire appraisal market; and the "freebie" appraisal provides a good example of interaction of motives and communication between appraiser and the appraisal customer.

The exact genesis of each "freebie" appraisal, while being different in each instance, has some generalities not too far from the average, especially since the subject of gems is mysterious to most people and appraisals are but a mere footnote to the subject of gems.

Finding themselves involved with an obscure facet of a mysterious business, most people are at a loss as to what to do, which is both natural and unfortunate. Floundering in the unfamiliar gem trade, people often times try to obtain free advice from retailers. The person seeking such advice can fall into any of the categories already discussed: the inheritor of gems; the recipient of a gift; a longtime owner of a gem; a person making the veiled offer to sell; or someone hoping to establish a market price for resale. However, the retailer sees a person asking, "What is this worth?" and knows the person could fit into any of the above categories, but he does not know which one. Also, other facts go unstated by the customer, such as being on unfamiliar ground; feeling at the mercy of the appraiser; knowing he might be taken advantage of; not knowing whether his gems worth $5 or $50,000; and above all, he does not want to spend a $25 to $200 appraisal fee on a gem that might be worthless.

While the customer finds himself in unfamiliar territory, so, too, the retailer-appraiser must deal with many unknown factors in the person of the "customer". Some well-seasoned retailers know how to defuse a problem situation like this and are willing to help, gratis. However, in some cases the ambiguities become impossible to resolve and the appraiser finds himself forced into a corner. At this point he must assume the "customer" is making a veiled offer to sell or trying to establish a market price for resale. The question, "What is this worth?" becomes translated into, "What will you give me for this stone?", or "What should I sell this gem for?" Neither question really qualifies under the appraisal heading. Also, there will be a large difference in the retail appraisal value given to the gem and the value assigned as an answer to either question.

If the gem were a recent purchase the retail value would probably be the original purchase price. In contrast, if the person wanted to sell the stone to the retailer, the retailer could not pay any more than he would pay his supplier for the stone. Otherwise he would be unable to resell the stone for the proper price. Anything less than a straightforward request for a formal appraisal sets off an alarm declaring the party wants to sell the stone. Suspecting this, the retailer, being put in a ticklish position, has an unclear situation to deal with and, most likely, responds with a similar lack of clarity. For one thing, if he discerns the desire to have his establishment buy the item, his estimate of value will most likely be less than wholesale. A *less* than wholesale offer is due to the fact that in buying from his wholesale supplier the retailer buys specific goods he knows he can sell, exactly when he wants to buy, at wholesale, and with generous financial terms.

However, when confronted with buying a random item, not necessarily needed at a specific time, with a vague idea of when it can be resold, the retailer must protect himself and his capital by buying low. He encounters a similar predicament when he thinks the customer is hot to sell -- not to him, but to the public. In this case, the person seeking advice puts himself in a position of being in competition with the retailer, and interests of self-preservation are liable to spring forth on the retailer's part.

As we can see, while many problems with the "freebie" appraisal are prevalent, mis-information stands first.

SUMMARY OF THE APPRAISAL SCENE

Looking at the variables involving the appraisal customer we can come to several conclusions: the customer cannot necessarily expect equal validity in each appraisal and he cannot expect them to be uniform. Appraisals are neither official nor can he expect the dollar value to mean the same thing at all times.

From the viewpoint of the appraiser we found other factors. The appraiser must have both adequate gemological knowledge and commercial knowledge. While the appraiser must be in the position of being a truly disinterested third party, we have seen there are frequently obstacles in retaining this pose: temptation to give out punitive appraisals and dealing with the veiled offer to sell. The appraiser must also be a person who maintains rigid quality control. Finally, we examined the problems facing the appraiser when asked for free advice.

PROBLEM-SOLVING BY THE TRADE

We now know there are many psychological factors involved in appraisals from all sides. Since the problems have existed for some time and have hindered the marketing of gemstones, some people in the trade are trying to solve these problems.

Over the past few years there have been several answers to appraisal problems which are new and somewhat innovative. For one thing, the emergence of nationally known gemstone experts who appraise gemstones on a nationwide basis, rather than only on a local basis, is a new concept.

Another emerging phenomenon is the gem trade laboratory. In this day and age, any good sized city will most likely have a trade laboratory. Of course, the laboratories of the GIA have been in existence for many years, giving substantive evaluations of colored stones and qualitative evaluations of diamonds. However, the new laboratories being discussed are different because some of them give dollar evaluations of the stones they examine. They are also different in that, with one or two exceptions, they are run purely as businesses, whereas the GIA labs are still wholly-owned subsidiaries of an overall non-profit educational institution. That these laboratories are businesses per-se does not denigrate them in any sense. We simply feel it is best for the public to know the nature of each type of organization to avoid confusion.

A momentary digression might help in understanding the kind of confusion to avoid. Claims are often heard that John Doe got an appraisal from the GIA. We want to dispel this myth herewith. There is no such thing as an appraisal from the GIA. A colored stone can receive a *certificate* stating its species and whether it is of synthetic or natural origin. A diamond can receive a certificate stating whether it is a diamond or an imitation. A stone determined to be a diamond will be graded for color, clarity, cut and be weighed. However, whether colored stone or diamond, no dollar value will be given on a GIA certificate. Therefore, no GIA *certificate* can legitimately be called an appraisal.

The third development in the appraisal area, and the most pervasive in sheer numbers, is the retail establishment with highly trained staff. The educational opportunities currently available, combined with the competitive nature of the gem trade and the genuine desire to increase professionalism, all seem to be working toward higher levels of competency. As we can see, the gemstone industry is rising in various ways to meet the challenge of providing proper appraisals to the public.

APPRAISALS:

THE COLLECTOR'S VIEWPOINT

Appropriately we leave the description of the appraisal scene on a positive note. The stance of the collector regarding appraisals has to be both positive and aggressive. The collector has to disabuse himself of the general public's viewpoint and modus operandi and circumvent any of the negative factors present from the appraiser's viewpoint. The collector must be an active not a passive agent.

Shopping for an appraiser becomes one of the active and positive ways a collector can influence the appraisal experience. The task of the collector as appraisal customer involves trying to assess the appraiser. Two of the most important aspects in evaluating an appraiser are the extent to which he is knowledgeable and how willing he is to remain an impartial third party.

Judging an appraiser presents difficulties to the novice. Impartiality is one such problem. Certain labs assure their impartiality by severely limiting contact with the appraisal customer. At such a lab you never meet the appraiser but are taken care of by a clerk. The only way to assess the knowledge of the appraiser at this type of lab would be either by reputation or through available literature. The appraiser who is available to the customer and also trades in stones creates a second dilemma. Impartiality in the case of an appraiser/dealer, while not assured by the physical layout of the business, helps in determining knowledgeability.

Knowledgeability becomes especially important when the gem in question is of exceptional quality because there will be very, very few people who can give an honest and accurate appraisal. The fact is, more appraisers are more competent in the middle to upper middle range of quality than the highest range. It would be a grave error to purchase a very, very fine gem from a dealer of highest caliber and then take the stone to a middle range appraiser whose knowledge and experience does not equal the stone. If this happens, the results are quite often disastrous for all concerned. Frequently the gem receives an under-valued appraisal. For some reason the collector seems to believe this low-ball appraisal, rather than believe he received a good deal from the supplier. Perhaps this is so because it is easier to believe we have been cheated than that a mistake has been made by someone purported to be an expert.

However, to be fair, we must give our supplier the same benefit of doubt we give the appraiser. A sad fact of our nature tends to believe a naysayer first and last, and to put an unreasonable burden of proof on the supplying agent. The key here would be to shop just as diligently for an appraiser with adequate knowledge as we shop for rare and very fine gemstones.

If shopping for knowledgeability is necessary, so, too, is finding an appraiser who takes pride in his work. Although also difficult to assess, observing the manner in which the appraisal is done gives a clue. An appraisal can be a quick eye-balling estimate or a studied inspection. In the same vein, there can be written or verbal appraisals. While each might be valid, somehow the overall tone and approach to the subject is different. Assuming the gemological identity of the stone is not in question, a quick eye-balling of the stone, followed by a verbal statement may very well be accurate. However, the question remains: Is the appraiser giving the appraisal his best? In contrast, it would seem the person taking his time and putting his views in writing carries more weight and would be giving the best he has to offer.

Now that you know some of the basics of appraising an appraiser, it should be easier to take an active role in the appraisal process. Remember, even as you make a choice, you are still shopping. Whether you are dealing with an individual, a lab or retailer, if you are not happy with the service, you still have the option of choosing someone else.

WORTH

As we say in the description of appraisals from the customer's standpoint, the dollar amount on the appraisal which represents worth may be different in the eye of different people. First and foremost, you as the collector must have your own very clear idea of what *you* want the appraisal to represent. Clarity on behalf of the customer should bring out clarity on behalf of the appraiser. In general, the dollar figure on an appraisal means the retail replacement value: the value at which the same item should be available from a retailer who routinely stocks equivalent merchandise. If this is the type of appraisal you want, make that fact clear. Also, make sure that the appraiser understands it and clearly and willingly makes that type of appraisal.

Although retail replacement value is the norm, there may be circumstances in which another type of appraisal is desired. In order to determine this we must ask four questions:

1. To whom is the stone in question worth how much?
2. Under what circumstances is the gem worth how much?
3. When is the gem worth how much?
4. According to whom is it worth X dollars?

The first of these questions points out the fact that a given gem might be worth different amounts to different people. For example, how much is it worth to your insurance company for reasonably easy replacement; how much to you if you care to buy a matching piece; how much would the piece cost the average retail customer; how much would the stone be worth for resale to a private party for adornment; how much would the stone be worth to the retailer; how much would the stone be worth to a wholesaler; how much would the stone be worth to a dealer? The true worth of any stone can be defined as the amount a willing buyer pays a willing seller, the difference being the identity of that person.

The next question, as to *when* the gem is worth how much, is simpler than the other questions. Any appraisal has to deal with the present. Estimates as to future worth of any item are, at best, educated guesses. Any guesses less than the best belong in the side-show, crystal-ball gazing category. At the other extreme, past value of merchandise does not relate to present day transactions.

If the worth of a gem, according to an appraisal, has a validity only for the present we can see all appraisals have a limited useful life. For purposes of resale a current appraisal should help obtain the highest current value possible -- everything else being equal. Likewise, for insurance purposes it would be a shame to lose a gem in 1995 with a 1985 appraisal.

The final question, according to *whom* is the stone worth X dollars, becomes a very important question for those collecting the highest quality gems. The very few stones that can really be rated as the highest quality are quite scarce. Assuming everyone giving appraisal advice has adequate knowledge of the highest quality can be a mistake. Therefore, the exposure of the appraiser has become important. Judging knowledgeability of lab-type appraisers in this respect can be difficult. This does not mean they are not qualified; it does mean it is difficult to distinguish between those who are and those who are not. On the other hand, an appraiser who is also a retailer may be more easily judged. By looking over his stock the collector can determine if he deals in goods of comparable quality and size. If so, he should be qualified to make an appraisal. One thing to remember, high quality gems are rare and valuable and finding an appraiser who is truly qualified to appraise them may take some effort -- but truly good advice is worth seeking in such an important matter.

With regard to the worth of a gem, we see its dollar value varies widely according to the exact conditions. The general concept of an appraisal has almost always been limited to retail replacement value. In many instances translating retail replacement value into the information you need at a given time may be difficult. There are nationally known appraisers who will give values other than retail replacement. Then, too, there may be local appraisers with whom you may be able to speak freely, who know the market, who will retain impartiality, and who will help you find the answer to the exact question of worth you are posing.

A MATTER OF OPINION

In discussing the worth of a stone we mostly reviewed and clarified what you as a collector may or may not want in an appraisal. In considering appraisals further we must cover one objective *fact* which has nothing to do with what we do or do not want from an appraisal. This fact is -- an appraisal is an opinion. Hopefully, we will clarify this point and demonstrate how you, the collector can deal with the opinion nature of an appraisal. When appraisals were done by the old fashioned, hand-hewn method, the nature of appraisals as opinions was supremely evident. However, with the advent of new methods, methods that are more streamlined and more assembly line in their manufacture, the opinion part of the appraisal submerges. The use of such things as comparison stones, systems of evaluation, reference to computer printouts, etc., make some of the newer appraisal systems seem opinion free. However, we must realize these new trappings only make appraisals more uniform in their application. While these methods are desirable and helpful, we must continue to be aware of the fact that the origin of any system had to be rife with opinions. The decision to use comparison stones and the choice of the particular stones was based on opinion. In the same way figuring out a complicated evaluation system and devising original computer programs were formed from opinions. Thus, all appraisals are opinions.

Earlier in this chapter we discussed three key factors to consider when appraisers use their knowledge.

Two of the factors, the knowledge possessed by the appraiser and his willingness to maintain a high quality product should be slightly modified to take into account the opinion-nature of appraisals as follows: "An appraisal is partially an *opinion* based on the knowledge of the appraiser and affected by his work habits." By using the word opinion as an additional modifier we want to stress that appraisals are not carved in stone nor do they take on manifestations of sacredness.

GEM EVALUATION:

WHAT'S IMPORTANT TO THE COLLECTOR?

The evaluation of gems always brings up the four "C's": color, clarity, carat weight and cut. The order in which we have put them is the way they are ranked in importance by most people with color being the most important. However, if any of the four "C's" is disproportionately bad in a stone it rules over the other factors. These are simple and general rules which really do not help the collector very much. By way of helping the collector we have created a new term which embraces all of the four "C's" and includes some new evaluation factors.

In order to maintain alphabetical symmetry we have decided to label this new factor "covetability." A one carat round brilliant D flawless diamond is a highly coveted gem. Yet some other diamonds are not quite as coveted. So, we can see that the word diamond in and of itself is not equal to covetability. To certain dealers and collectors a 15 carat flawless chrome tourmaline with a highly saturated green color is highly coveted. If the same stone were olive in color it would not be so coveted. And so it goes within each variety of gemstone.

Now, to complicate matters, we have to point out that inequalities in the covetability factor not only occur within a gem variety but also occur from variety to variety. Using the two stones we just described, we see that the one carat round brilliant D flawless diamond has a higher covetability rating than the 15 carat chrome tourmaline. That is to say, it would have a higher rating on an objective scale acceptable to most collectors. Subjectively, there are some people who would rather own the tourmaline. However, the diamond would, under most market conditions, sell more readily within the trade at a higher price than the tourmaline. If it were possible, and it may become possible in a few years, to accurately describe covetability, all gems would become equally tradeable if properly graded and priced. The covetability rating of a given stone is almost never adequately communicated in an appraisal.

RARITY

If we describe covetability as tradeability, desirability, and by the other words and phrases we used, we must also try to understand what creates covetability. What attributes of a gem make it covetable? To understand this we must first break down the word covetable. The verb "to covet" means to want something a great deal that belongs to someone else. Now, when we generalize this to all gemstones and all people in the gem market, we must ask, "What gems are the most wanted by the most people?" One of the more commonly discussed aspects of gems that should shed some light on this question is rarity.

MINERAL RARITY

Rarity as an individual subject deserves a great deal of discussion because rarity in gemstones is not all that simple a matter. First we have what we will call "mineral rarity." Some minerals are rarer than others. For example, quartz and feldspar occur more often than grossular garnet or diamond. Even more specifically, some minerals form gem quality crystals more rarely than others. From our previous example, quartz and feldspar are two of the most common minerals in the earth's crust, yet quartz forms gem quality crystals much more commonly than feldspar.

SIZE RARITY

Continuing with the concept of mineral rarity, we can begin to bring in that quality described by the traditional four "C's". First, let's take carats, or size. Within any given species of gem, we tend to find more small, cuttable crystals than large, cuttable crystals. Therefore, large stones of any variety are rarer, less available, and therefore more coveted than small stones. The occurrence and characteristics of diamond are so well documented in this regard that tables exist showing the relative value of diamonds equal in all respects except size. However, what is not as well documented are the same occurrences and characteristics for any of the other gemstones. For this reason, people may not realize that the size occurrences for one mineral are usually not the same as for another. Spinel and andalusite rarely, if ever, come in big sizes. A forty carat spinel or a thirty carat andalusite is extremely rare, rarer perhaps than a sapphire of the same size. In mineralogical contrast to spinel or andalusite we have the mineral beryl (aquamarine, morganite, heliodor, emerald). With the noted exception of fine emerald, beryl tends to occur in larger crystals more commonly than many other minerals. Fine aquamarines are readily available, if not common, up to 100 carats in size.

Size rarity can also vary from variety to variety within a species. A good example of this occurs within the chrysoberyl family. The *variety* of chrysoberyl known as alexandrite not only occurs less frequently than common chrysoberyl but also when it does occur, it tends to occur in smaller sizes.

COLOR RARITY

Color rarity represents yet another aspect of covetability, similar in many ways to size rarity. For any given variety of gemstone there is usually a market preference for specific colors. In most instances the market preference is simply based on a common perception of beauty. In other cases, the market preference is based simply on exposure. Not many people know about golden orange tourmaline. The gold color tourmaline is rarer and to those who have seen it, extremely exciting and desirable. But, rubellite as a known color has more market preference.

Whatever the reason for preference, either simple beauty or market preference, the net results are the same. Once a color optimum has been decided, only a few stones fit that description. all other stones are judged relative to the optimum color; this judging occurs in different ways. Within a gem variety the optimum is based on a specific hue and intensity of color. In our previous example, rubellite tourmalines, the market prefers an intense ruby red. Deviation from that optimum can arise in the form of hue deviation (impure color) or intensity deviation (too light -- too dark). Price adjustments are made in the market for either or both kinds of deviation. Color judgment also comes in the form of preferred hues within a species. For instance, we separate tsavorite garnet from all other grossularite based solely on color. Grossulars occur in several color varieties, tsavorite being the green variety. A golden grossular of equal intensity and purity of color, of equal size and other characteristics, will bring less than a tsavorite. The market has a preference for *green* grossular garnets over *gold* grossular garnets. Out of all the grossular garnets mined, only a few are green. Of those few which are green, even fewer are a pure, intense green. When the market has a preference for a specific color and a specific state of purity intensity for that color, it is easy to see why the concept of color rarity exists. We can also see with equal ease how color rarity affects and becomes a factor in covetability.

CLARITY RARITY

Of the remaining two "C's", clarity represents another important factor in covetability. We describe clarity as the "flawless" grading in a D *flawless* diamond. The word "clean" and its derivation "cleanliness" are sometimes used when discussing clarity.

So far we have talked about "size rarity" and "color rarity." Well, we can now add the rhyming phrase, "clarity rarity." Again, as with color, clarity rarity differs from species to species and variety to variety. Some minerals tend to yield clean stones more than others. Almost everyone familiar with stones knows that diamonds are severely graded down for lack of clarity and that emeralds are accepted with a few inclusions. This type of grading differential exists throughout the mineral world. Rubellite tourmalines tend to have inclusions. But the important point we want to make is that the cleaner a stone, the higher its covetability rating. Everybody would love to own a flawless emerald but since they cannot, the market bids up those emeralds with the fewest inclusions. Everyone would like to own flawless diamonds, but the miners could not afford to sell just inclusion-free diamonds and again, the market bids up inclusion-free diamonds. The bidding process implies relatively few gems are close to being inclusion-free while the majority tend to have inclusions in varying degrees. Needless to say, the covetability rating of flawless or near flawless gems is much higher than for moderately or heavily included stones.

CUTTING RARITY

Again, as with the other factors that make up covetability, there are differences in the importance of cutting from gem variety to gem variety. These differences are the subtle specifics that are good for the collector to learn. However, the broad rule is that there are fewer well cut gems and more poorly cut gems. This broad rule tells us we have a phenomenon we can label "cutting rarity." The collector must perceive cutting rarity as an additional consideration in covetability.

MARKET PREFERENCE

In addition to mineral rarity and rarity associated with each of the traditional four "C's" there is an aspect of covetability which has to do with current market trends. Certain very rare gem varieties have disproportionately low prices and in some instances are so rare a market price cannot be established. For example, benitoite, a truly beautiful gem, is so very rare only rare-stone collectors are aware of its existence. Rarity does not insure value. The market must actively desire and be looking for a gem of its rarity to be adequately appreciated. Changing market trends are an important aspect to "covetability," which can be seen by the market moving from species to species to species as gem sources run low. Spinel was overlooked for years despite its beauty and rarity but began to be appreciated by the market by 1980. Tsavorite and tanzanite were unknown 25 years ago and their "covetability" increased as they established their place in the market.

Now that we have enumerated the components of covetability individually, we must consider them together. Every single gemstone has a covetability rating in all of the individual aspects. The sum of all these individual ratings constitutes the overall covetability of a gemstone. Since, as we add qualifications to a stone each time we grade it on one rating factor, we see the extent to which a stone rating well in all factors increases in rarity. The laws of statistics as applied to naturally occurring substances tells us that there is only a certain small percentage of gems rating high in all respects.

VI

GETTING ACQUAINTED WITH INCLUSIONS

The serious collector should know something about inclusions. However, it is with some trepidation that we take up this subject. Why? The subject of inclusions is, in gemstones, the quintessential example of how a little knowledge can be dangerous. All gems have inclusions. The standard definition of "flawless" in gems is "free of inclusions at 10X magnification". Implicit in the definition is the fact that given enough magnification there will be imperfections.

Most serious gem collectors enjoy collecting the broad spectrum of gem species, varieties, and colors. Taking into account all the variations generated by all the species, varieties and colors, then multiplying this by the additional factor of size, there are some real difficulties in assessing the clarity of all gems. This fact is made apparent by the fact that there is no overall grading system for colored stones that is as accepted as the grading systems that exist for diamonds. What is acceptable for andalusite is not acceptable for aquamarine. This much is known and accepted by the gem trade but may not be codified by any grading system.

Despite the size of this problem we would like to tackle it in this chapter. We are not trying to set up a grading system. What we would like to do is consider some of the gem species, varieties, and color variations and speak to their individual natures as related to inclusions. The issue of clarity of diamonds is taken up in the chapter on diamonds.

There are some general rules regarding what is and what is not acceptable in colored stones:

Eye clean -- The general standard in grading colored stones carries the label "eye clean". If a stone has no defects visible to the unaided eye it is a good stone. There are exceptions to this rule but it is a good rule to remember. The point of having a clean stone is that its beauty is not impeded by defects. In an eye clean stone light will pass relatively freely into and back out of a stone and have some brilliancy. Beauty is the rule, rules are not the rule.

Color intensity -- As a rule, the gem trade accepts more inclusions in dark stones as opposed to pastel colored stones. This is simply a matter of fact that dark colors hide inclusions to a certain degree. In pastel colored stones inlcusions are visible at a lower threshold than in dark stones. This fact may or may not be recorded in any gem grading manual but it is a fact of life in the buying and selling of gems. This fact gets back to the original reason we like gems--beauty--and the point at which inclusions impinge on the beauty of a stone.

Rarity -- As a rule, rare stones are more accepted with inclusions than common stones. As an example a two carat alexandrite with some slightly visible inclusions might be worth many thousands of dollars while a two carat blue topaz worth a few tens of dollars should be free from visible flaws. While this may seem so sensible and obvious on the one hand, consider the fact that you will be paying more money for rare stones. As a collector you will often be paying more for stones that have more inclusions--seems backwards doesn't it.

Size -- Larger stones are usually accepted with more inclusions than smaller stones. For instance a 7x5mm oval andalusite (approx. .75ct) should be pretty well flaw free while a 10 carat andalusite is so unusual it might well be accepted with eye visible inclusions if they are not too obtrusive. In a sense this is a corollary to the aspect of rarity. Larger stones are more rare than smaller stones. However, the distribution of size varies with each gem species and variety so the size issue has its own ramifications in each gem species, variety, and color.

Orientation -- Inclusions not eye visible from the top but visible from the side or bottom are less offensive than inclusions visible from the top of the stone. Since most gems are mounted into jewelry and since most jewelry holds a stone so it is mostly visible from the top, inclusions not visible from the top are somewhat less important.

INCLUSIONS -- STONE BY STONE

At this point we would like to turn to the individual variety of gemstones to discuss them one by one with their inherent inclusions. To avoid the appearance of bias in encouraging you to buy one gem over another, we will list each gemstone alphabetically. Since some species can be broken down into distinct varieties and since some species will have a multiplicity of inclusion types, it may seem one type of gemstone is receiving more coverage than another. However, this is motivated by a desire to be thorough in discussing inclusions rather than to show favoritism.

ANDALUSITE

ANDALUSITE: GENERAL COMMENTS

Acceptance with inclusions: Andalusite is a middle of the road gem. It is accepted with more inclusions than a blue topaz, or aquamarine but not as accepted with inclusions as an emerald or rubellite. Eye clean is a good rule for average size andalusite.

Size considerations: Andalusite is an extreme example of a stone that doesn't often occur in large sizes. To get a large stone a collector may have to compromise a bit on clarity. Not too much mind you but somewhat.

Color considerations: There is no specific color of andalusite that is so sought after in comparison with other colors of andalusite that color is a consideration in the acceptance of inclusions.

Andalusite inclusions, specific things to look for:
Andalusite, comes largely from deposits in Brazil. Since andalusite usually comes to the gem cutter in the form of water-worn crystals, cutting out problem inclusions is a

real challenge for the cutter. Also, since cut andalusite is rare in sizes exceeding two carats, it is always a temptation for the cutter to cut as large a stone as possible. There is additional temptation since the price per-carat increases dramatically with increases in size. Andalusite is a very attractive, pleochroic gem.

The first problem is called wispy-veils. These type of veil inclusions are different from other types of veil inclusions in other stones because the component parts of the veil are not as gross in appearance as in other stones. These veils are very gossamer in appearance. Because of their wispy/gossamer nature they are, in certain cases, left in the stone. Sometimes they are left in and it does not really detract from the overall appearance of the stone. However, if one of them is in the wrong part of the stone, the entire appearance of the stone can be spoiled. Look very closely for these veils because their existence can fool even the closest examiner. However, not all andalusites have this particular problem. We have to say, in some cases, a very good andalusite may have a very minor wispy veil and be a good stone. In this case, it is a matter of judgment as to the exact extent to which a particular inclusion may or may not be acceptable.

The second, and also a very subtle type of inclusion found in andalusite, is very fine needles. These needles are very likely rutile crystal inclusions which are very common in silicate stones. Rutile, although itself not a silicate, seems to be associated with silicate minerals. The variety of needles occurring in andalusite are usually particularly fine and small in diameter, making them inobtrusive in finished stones. A perfectly wonderful appearing stone might have these inclusions which are not noticeable without careful examination.

A third type of inclusion found in andalusite is open cleavages. Andalusite does have distinct cleavage in one direction. Usually an open cleavage in a stone is only observable if light hits the cleavage just right. Since cleavages are what we would call planar (that is existing in a plane) if they are oriented a certain way in a stone, they are not visible. Looking at a cleavage can be likened to looking at a very thin sheet of glass submerged in a glass of water. If you look at it in most directions, you will either see right through it and not know it is there, or if observed in the cross section, it is so narrow that it is difficult to detect. However, if you were to take a very thin sheet of glass submerged in water and shine a light on it in exactly the right manner, the reflection of light from the sheet of glass would cause you to know very definitely that it was present. You can imagine that to get light to reflect from a sheet of glass submerged in water, you would have to play the light over the entire container of water from many different directions. Such is the case with finding an open cleavage in a cut stone. This is perhaps one of the most difficult types of inclusions to find in any stone. However, once you have had some experience, it is not too terribly difficult to figure out. By orienting the stone very carefully in regard to the light, you will cause the cleavage plane to reflect through the stone and it will demonstrate a shiny appearance. If you see this and the shiny reflections are not normal reflections of facets, you will know you are looking at a stone in which an open cleavage exists. To leave such a cleavage in a gem usually structurally weakens the stone and decreases the value.

As a guide to collecting we should point out that, except for cleavage problems, a 10 carat andalusite with a small veil or a small needle in one corner is more acceptable and more valuable than a five carat absolutely clean stone. This is especially so, as we pointed out, because andalusite rarely occurs in large sizes. This is particularly true in andalusite versus many other gemstone varieties.

BERYL

AQUAMARINE: GENERAL COMMENTS

Acceptance with inclusions: Aquamarine should generally be free of eye visible inclusions.

Size considerations: In contrast to andalusite aquamarine is one of those stones which produces large gems on a regular basis. Not only are the aqua stones available in large sizes but in clean stones in large sizes. Due to the generally pastel nature of the color in aquamarine flaws usually are quite visible. An aqua should be a clean stone whatever the size.

Color considerations: Although the darker shades of aquamarine are quite rare and coveted aquamarine should still be eye clean even in the premium grades.

Aquamarine inclusions, specific things to look for:
The mineral beryl comes in at least three gemstone varieties. The three varieties are aquamarine, emerald and morganite.

Of the three beryls, aquamarine is probably the most common. Although more common than morganite, aquamarine commands higher prices. This may be due to the fact that aquamarine has a color which is appreciated by most people and because there has been enough of it available for successful promotion for a number of years. The two primary problem inclusions in aquamarine are tubular inclusions and what is referred to here as "bubble" veils.

Tubular inclusions in aquamarine are the less common problem. These tubes run parallel to the "C" axis of the crystal. In unusual instances, when they occur abundantly enough in aquamarine, a cat's-eye aquamarine can be fashioned from the rough. More commonly, though, not enough tubes exist to cut a cat's-eye, but enough do exist to diminish the value of the finished stone. Aquamarine is generally accepted by the trade only in very clean stones. Any stone you consider collecting should be as free as possible from this type of inclusion. These tubular inclusions are usually smaller in size than those found in other types of gemstones. Because of this, and because they also may be lightly dispersed in a stone, they are sometimes not readily visible. Then too, it is possible to orient them perpendicular to the table of the stone, thereby rendering them much less visible when examining a stone in a non-professional manner. These inclusions are labeled tubes and described as tubes simply because they are long, rod-like or cylindrical inclusions that are either vacant or have gas inside much like the tube of a fluorescent lamp.

The other problem inclusions in aquamarine, "bubble" veils, are perhaps more apparent than the wispy veils in andalusite but they still can be difficult to spot at times. These veils are not actually made up of individual bubbles, but are really negative crystals or some other types of inclusions. They do, however, look like bubbles and if you think of them this way, you will be more likely to see them. They can be obvious at times, but at other times they can occur in such small sizes so they are virtually undetectable. You can detect this inclusion by very carefully lighting your stone for proper inspection and by rotating it with care. Be sure to look at the stone from every possible angle.

EMERALD: GENERAL COMMENTS

Acceptance with inclusions: Emerald is the best known example of a stone that is accepted with eye visible inclusions. Emeralds are the result of a very rare co-existence of chromium (the coloring agent) and beryllium (emerald is a beryl). So rare is this combination in nature that emeralds are rare. For some reason they very rarely form into crystals which cut eye clean gems. If we want this vivid color in our lives we have to accept it with inclusions.

Size considerations: Not only is emerald rare but it rarely forms into large crystals like other beryls. Aquamarine and morganite can form into huge crystals, not emerald. The larger the emerald the rarer it is. Larger emeralds are accepted with more eye visible inclusions than smaller emeralds.

Color considerations: The value of emerald is very affected by color. To knowledgeable people in the trade a rare and prized color in emerald is excuse enough to accept a few more inclusions. Conversely, an exceptionally clean emerald is forgiven having a color that varies from the optimum.

Emerald inclusions, specific things to look for: Since it is beryl, as is aquamarine, emerald has some of the same problems as aquamarine. Emerald can have tubes.

In fact there are examples of cat's-eye emerald, although quite rare. The main problem in emeralds is in determining whether or not the inclusions in any way affect the structural integrity of the stone. Virtually all emeralds have inclusions, a fact which is accepted by the market. However, there are instances in which emeralds are sold when the stones have cracks or such an abundance of veils or other inclusions that they may not be strong enough. This is a judgment matter and renders the problem a little bit more difficult. Crack type inclusions usually manifest themselves in much the same way as the open cleavages which we described in andalusite. Technically speaking, emerald does not have easy, perfect cleavage, although some people might refer to a crack as a cleavage. There is a difference between the two, but it is more of a scientific distinction rather than a pragmatic one. To find a crack in a stone you must use the same procedures as finding an open cleavage. Hold a stone and rotate it very slowly to see if you can spot any shiny areas. If you find any such areas, which are not facet reflections, you can be suspicious that the stone has a crack in it. Once you have found a crack, it will be up to you to determine its effect on the stone. A small crack might not be too harmful to the strength of the emerald. If it goes through a large portion of the stone, you might want to consider buying another emerald.

Since, as we say, most emeralds have inclusions, many producers of emeralds treat the emeralds with oil to hide fractures. If you are worried about the quality of emeralds offered to you, please consult a competent gemologist.

MORGANITE: GENERAL COMMENTS

Acceptance with inclusions: Morganite is somewhere between aquamarine and emerald for acceptability with inclusions. Morganite is a fairly rare stone. Individual mines can produce a large quantity of morganite from time to time usually followed by a lack of material for a long time. In this sense it appears that morganite is less available than aquamarine. Perhaps that is why it is forgiven a few more inclusions than is aqua.

Size considerations: There is a certain degree to which a smaller morganite is held to a higher standard of cleanliness than a larger one. However, on the occasions that morganite is produced, it does furnish a fair number of large stones. Due to this fact a large morganite doesn't get the forgiveness a large emerald might.

Color considerations: Virtually all morganite comes in colors that might be considered pale. Due to this, the variation that does occur does not affect the acceptance of flaws.

Morganite inclusions, specific things to look for:
Morganite is perhaps one of the most underrated gems, not only in the beryl family, but in the gem field generally. Morganite of good color is exceedingly rare. Perhaps this is the reason it has not attained higher prices. Most people are familiar only with inferior morganite and therefore assume that all morganite lacks beauty and therefore lacks value. Morganite is susceptible to bubble-like inclusions. While similar in some ways to the "bubble" veils in aquamarine, they are distinctly different in morganite. In aquamarine the "bubble" veils tend to

locate in a cohesive mass, in morganite the individual inclusions are often dispersed throughout the entire stone, with the random spacing of no particular pattern. A morganite can have a relatively large clean area, but with one or two inclusions which can spoil the entire stone. Through careful examination, you can easily see if you have a nice stone. Depending upon the exact intensity of color and general clarity, one or two small inclusions are acceptable in morganite. If you hold out for a clean stone of fine color, you will undoubtedly be pleased that you did.

CHRYSOBERYL

COMMON CHRYSOBERYL: GENERAL COMMENTS

Acceptance with inclusions: First let us digress a moment to comment on the term "common chrysoberyl" The word "common" is used to distinguish normal faceted chrysoberyl from cats-eye and alexandrite. There is nothing "common" about it. Chrysoberyl is rare. As regards to the acceptability of chrysoberyl with inclusions we have to say that the rarity of chrysoberyl generally gives it more leeway than many other gems are allowed. In this respect chrysoberyl is a middle of the pack gem like andalusite or sapphire.

Size considerations: Chrysoberyl is one of those stones that just does not occur in big sizes--especially in clean facetable pieces. One large chrysoberyl that we personally cut and sold is currently on display in a prominent museum. That particular stone has a few inclusions on one side that would not be accepted in an aquamarine. Fortunately the high refractive index and other optical properties of chrysoberyl have the tendency to confound the eye of the onlooker and hide inclusions that might be apparent in another type of gem.

Color considerations: While there are certain colors of chrysoberyl that are more alluring than others, none of the color stands out in a way to bring a sufficient premium to create further acceptance of additional inclusions.

Chrysoberyl inclusions, specific things to look for: Chrysoberyl not only follows beryl in our alphabetical list, but also mimics beryl in name. While the so-called "common" chrysoberyl is not particularly well known, the mineral chrysoberyl is better known in the form referred to as cat's-eye and the form referred to as alexandrite. Common chrysoberyl can be fashioned into faceted gems usually in its yellow, yellow-green, or brown colors. It represents a very good gemstone from the standpoint of durability, being 8 1/2 in hardness. Only corundum and diamond are harder.

COMMON CHRYSOBERYL

Although a relatively trouble-free stone from the standpoint of durability, the collector must be wary of the problem inclusion known as "silk" in faceted chrysoberyl. It is this silk which causes the chatoyancy in cat's-eye. However, if it is not cut out of a faceted stone, silk can cause a stone to be *sleepy*, that is to lose its brilliancy. The silk in chrysoberyl being very fine, finer by far than the tubes in beryl, does not diminish the value of a faceted stone if only a small amount remains. This is especially so if the cutter of the stone orients this small amount of silk perpendicular to the table so that it becomes almost completely unobservable. Again, we have a matter of judgment as to how much in the way of inclusion is acceptable for collecting a gem. Part of the answer to this is definitely the extent to which the stone is sleepy. The key to whether a stone would be acceptable or not acceptable is whether it is sleepy or not. If it is bright, crisp and shiny with a few minor bits of silk, it will probably serve as a good collection piece.

ALEXANDRITE: GENERAL COMMENTS

Acceptance with inclusions: Alexandrite is the rarest of all the birthstones. Not only does alexandrite enjoy special status as a birthstone but it also is especially coveted in the Orient, particularly Japan. This fact brings enormous price pressure on this stone which almost does not exist in the crust of the earth. Due to this fact alexandrite finds acceptance in clarity grades that would not be accepted in other gems. It is hard to compare the extent to which it is accepted with other gems such as emerald or rubellite that are known to have inclusions. Since alexandrite does produce eye clean stones from time to time, heavily included stones are marked down in price by comparison. However, since there are so few alexandrite stones in the market at any one time finding any quantifiable market consensus seems impossible.

Size considerations: All alexandrite stones are so rare that they seem to be given allowances at all sizes. Since alexandrite is one of those stones that occur only in small sizes it would seem that bigger ones should be given more allowances. However, they are all so rare they all seem to be given allowances whatever the size.

Color considerations: It would definitely seem that premium color alexandrites are given more leeway than average or poor color stones when it comes to accepting inclusions.

Alexandrite inclusions, specific things to look for:
Since alexandrite is the same mineral as common chrysoberyl, it has the same problems. Particularly common in the alexandrite variety of chrysoberyl are stones which have unacceptable amounts of silk. In some stones this is very evident and in others it is not. The proper method for examining for silk is to put the stone under a light in a rather normal examining position and rolling the light over the stone in such a way as to catch any reflection of the light from the silk. If this occurs you will note that the silk is reflected back as a light and shiny area of the stone that has a color lighter than the body color or color lighter than the reflection from facets. In some stones this is particularly difficult to find.

CAT'S EYE: GENERAL COMMENTS

Acceptance with inclusions: There are certain inclusions that can occur in cat's eye that ruin the stone in sufficient quantity. Cracks and veil-type inclusions are common to cat's eye. Depending on the size and severity of these inclusions the cat's eye may or may not be acceptable. Since the cat's eye effect is itself created by inclusions other inclusions can at times be successfully hidden and not affect the beauty of the stone.

Size considerations: Cat's eye is a rare gem. Although it has the same color range as facetable chrysoberyl, cat's eye is very nearly as rare as alexandrite. Large cat's eye does occur by comparison to alexandrite but not by comparison to other gems. Large stones are allowed some forgiveness but it is difficult to plot out just the extent to which this is true.

Color considerations: Top colors in cat's eye bring a substantial premium. As such, top color stones are given allowances other stones are not. Again, as with size considerations, cat's eye is so rare that its market cannot be well plotted, measured, and put on a graph.

Cat's eye inclusions, specific things to look for: Silk is not the problem in cat's-eye, rather it is the benefit. You would be better off to have an abundance rather than a lack of silk. The particular problem inclusions found in cat's-eye are cracks. For some reason a lot of this material has minor cracks in it which are very similar in nature to the open cleavages we discussed earlier. One advantage in being able to see a crack in a cat's-eye versus a faceted stone is that virtually none of the stone has reflecting faces. Any shiny reflections you see are rather easy to spot and to determine whether or not they are cracks.

CORUNDUM

CORUNDUM: GENERAL COMMENTS

Acceptance with inclusions:

1. Ruby: After alexandrite ruby is perhaps the rarest of the birthstones. Ruby is also one of the best known stones since antiquity. By being red it also happens to be one of those colors most attractive to human beings. The nature of ruby is to come in small crystals when it is clean enough to facet. All of these factors combine to make ruby accepted with a fair number of inclusions. Since ruby can be quite expensive some of the grading of ruby amounts to splitting hairs. If there are eye visible inclusions, where are they in the stone and how big are they? Also, ruby is generally a dark color in contrast with some other stones like aquamarine or chrysoberyl. The darker color can hide inclusions that might make another stone unappealing.

2. Sapphire: Although sapphire is corundum as is ruby there are some differences other than color. For our purposes here we will speak to blue sapphire as well as the fancy colors of pink and yellow. While sapphire crystals do not occur in the large sizes associated with beryl or colorless topaz or rubellite tourmaline, sapphire crystals do occur regularly in larger sizes than ruby and in bigger quantities and from more locations. For this reason the standards for clarity of sapphire are slightly more strict than for ruby. However, sapphire is allowed a fair amount of leeway when it comes to inclusions in comparison to aquamarine, or citrine, or topaz.

Size considerations:
1. Ruby: As we mentioned above ruby does not come in large facetable crystals. For this reason larger stones are rare and prized. Larger pieces are granted a fair amount of acceptability despite inclusions--depending upon how the inclusions affect the beauty of the stone. This type of grading can appear to be somewhat subjective. However if a dealer is consistently off center from the market consensus he will not be around long. There are some good grading systems around. However, none of them has achieved the popularity of the well known diamond grading systems.

2. Sapphire: Size considerations are important for sapphire as well. However since sapphire does produce larger gems than ruby and since there are more sources of sapphire than ruby the rules for sapphire are more strict than for ruby.

Color considerations:

1. Ruby: Fine color counts for a lot in ruby. Top Burmese red receives a lot of leeway for inclusions as compared to low color grade Thai stones.

2. Sapphire: Ironically, low color grade sapphire gets a break when it comes to inclusions--simply because it is too dark. Most poor color sapphire is considered poor color because it is dark midnight blue. This depth of color hides a multitude of inclusions. Top color sapphire gets a break too when it comes to inclusions--but not nearly the same break as ruby.

RUBY AND SAPPHIRE

Corundum inclusions, specific things to look for: In this day of very fine synthetic rubies and sapphires, it seems that having some inclusions in a stone is almost a blessing to verify natural origin. However, beyond having a few small inclusions for that purpose, it is nice to have a stone whose beauty and appearance is not marred by inclusions. There are three kinds of inclusions which can especially hurt the appearance of a fine ruby or sapphire and be fairly difficult to see with a quick glance. The first of these inclusions is exactly the same one that caused a problem in chrysoberyl and alexandrite -- silk. As you know, rubies and sapphires come in both faceted stones and star stones. The abundant existence of silk enables the star stone to have a star. Unfortunately, though, nature did not separate future star crystals from future facetable crystals. Many ruby and sapphire crystals form without enough silk to show a star but with enough silk to inhibit the play of light through the stone. Since the silk in corundums tends toward fineness in nature, just as the silk in chrysoberyl, this makes it difficult at times to detect its existence. However, to find unwanted silk in a faceted stone, hold the stone in your fingers or tweezers and let the light play over the stone as you rotate the stone. Keep rolling the light over the stone and keep changing the position of the stone. Look at both the crown of the stone and the pavilion. It may take some time, or you may find the silk very quickly. When you do find it, the silk will appear as an area of sheen with slightly different color from the body color of the stone. Again, as with chrysoberyl, one way of determining if a stone is likely to have silk is in assessing whether it is sleepy or not. Of course, sleepy stones will not show much brilliance and therefore something has to be interfering with the light. In many cases it will be silk or it could be something else.

The second type of inclusion we can find in corundum is growth lines. Growth lines are caused either by twinning (growth of two crystals into one crystal) or by a process where a single crystal grows for a while, stops growing and then continues. In either case there is a discontinuity in the growth of the stone that manifests itself visibly to the eye. The most remarkable examples of these growth lines occur in corundums from the Umba River Valley in Tanzania. Some of these stones look as though they have a set of internal venetian blinds. Yet, growth lines can occur in corundums from any locality so beware. Finding growth lines is much like looking for open cleavages or cracks in other stones we have mentioned.

GARNET

In considering garnet we will speak of grossular garnet, rhodolite garnet, and spessartite garnet.

GROSSULAR GARNET: GENERAL COMMENTS

Acceptance with inclusions: When taking up the subject of grossular garnet there is tsavorite and then there is everything else. Tsavorite is the pure, intense green stone which comes from East Africa. Tsavorite is rare, and sought after by rare-gem collectors and by jewelry aficionados as well. Its rarity has forced people to accept it with inclusions so long as the inclusions are not too obtrusive. The other colors of grossular garnet are rare as well but not as sought after. The market tends to be more strict with these colors.

Size considerations: Most commerically mined grossular garnet currently comes from East Africa. The formations in which they are found are metamorphic. That is to say, the original crystals formed in ground that was submerged beneath the surface of the Earth under other formations and then re-surfaced. The metamorphic process broke most of the original crystals into small broken shards. For this reason most grossular garnet from this area produces small gems. Larger stones are prized and are forgiven inclusions that would not be acceptable in aquamarine, or green tourmaline. Though less expensive, a five carat grossular garnet is probably as rare as a five carat ruby.

Color considerations: As mentioned above, when it comes to color in grossular garnet there is tsavorite and then there is everything else. In the categories that comprise "everything else" most of the stones are equally appreciated and therefore do not receive special preference when it comes to inclusions. Tsavorite is different. Top colors of tsavorite are allowed more in the way of inclusions than inferior colors. This has to do with the fact that these colors are in demand. Undoubtedly, the fact that premium colors of tsavorite are dark enough to hide at least some inclusions makes some difference as well.

Grossular garnet inclusions, specific things to look for: Of all the garnets, the grossular garnet enjoys the greatest current popularity for collecting. The primary source of this material is currently Kenya and Tanzania in East Africa. This material, especially the green variety, has become exceedingly popular in recent years. The green variety is especially well known by its trade name, "tsavorite." This material comes from the mines in a form which is very challenging for the cutter. It virtually never occurs in whole crystal forms because it occurs in metamorphic areas. During the metamorphosis breakage of the crystals occurred. Not immediately observable is the fact that many of the fractures, which are on the surface of the rough stones, actually continue into the interior of the stones. The cutters face a task of producing a stone without fractures, but this is sometimes difficult given the nature of the material. East African grossular characteristically comes in small sizes; larger stones bringing a very considerable premium. For this reason, there is always a temptation to cut a stone as large as possible out of every piece of rough. Unfortunately, this sometimes results in the cutters leaving in a fracture. To examine for these stones fractures, use the same techniques outlined for looking for open cleavages. Fractures, although they are not cleavages, appear much the same way as cleavages, and become immediately observable with proper lighting and handling.

A less common occurrence in grossular garnets is the presence of needles. While needles are exceedingly common in almost all other garnets, they are much more unusual in the grossular garnet species, especially garnets from Kenya and Tanzania. It is possible that their uncommoness makes them particularly deceptive to the potential buyer. If the needles are the small type which create asterism in other types of garnets, and if there is a sufficient number of needles in the stone, it can actually create a sleepy look, much like the sleepy look in star ruby or star sapphire. It seems needles show up more often in the green variety of the grossular garnet -- tsavorite, as opposed to the fancy colors -- the oranges, yellows, light yellows and light green colors. A sleepy look in a stone triggers the first hint of needles as well. This could be more commonly the result of veil-type inclusion, but can be caused by needles. While veils are common to tsavorite, and therefore are not an unexpected problem, if you have a sleepy stone, but can't find a veil, then you should be thinking of looking for needles. Sometimes there are not enough needles to make a stone sleepy and a cursory examination of a stone might not reveal their existence. Again the easy way to check for needles requires you to hold the stone in your fingers beneath an intense light and move the stone so that the light moves over the surface. This is the same technique we used in checking for silk in rubies and sapphires. Keep moving the position of the stone in your fingers. If there are sufficient number of needles you will eventually see a sheen. This sheen is a dead giveaway that there are needles. If the sheen effect is difficult to produce and all other factors of the stone are top quality, it may still be worth buying.

Needles that are thick can be seen individually by the naked eye. Also visible to the naked eye are clumps of very fine needles.

RHODOLITE GARNET

RHODOLITE GARNET: GENERAL COMMENTS

Acceptance with inclusions: Although rhodolite garnet is more rare and more expensive than other garnets in the red part of the spectrum it is not a rare stone. Rhodolite garnet should generally be eye clean, especially when viewed from the top.

Size considerations: Although rhodolite garnet regularly produces medium sized gems, bigger stones especially over 5 carats are becoming more difficult to obtain. Sometimes a particularly fine specimen might exhibit some sheen produced by needle type inclusions. Depending on the color and other considerations larger stones are given some leeway.

Color considerations: The more prized colors of rhodolite are generally lighter in color. Due to this preference better color rhodolites are not really going to be forgiven additional inclusions--lighter colored stones show inclusions more readily.

Rhodolite garnet, specific things to look for:

Although far more common than the grossular garnets, rhodolite garnet is one of the loveliest and most popular garnets. Current production comes primarily from Tanzania, although there are other rhodolite garnet localities. The main problem in buying rhodolite garnets is the presence of needle-like inclusions we mentioned as being unusual in grossular garnets. True to the majority of garnet varieties, rhodolite garnets commonly have this type of inclusion. The needles in rhodolite go in two directions at angles to each other and if they occurred in sufficient quantity they would cause a four-ray star garnet. Unfortunately, they almost never do occur in sufficient quantities to star, but only in sufficient quantities to make a sleepy stone. Rhodolite obtained in Tanzania usually has these inclusions. When only a few needles occur they give the appearance of a perfectly clean stone, since they do not obstruct the light very much. Also, since most of these stones do have a few needles, buying pivots on turning down any stone which is particularly full of needles. We do this by comparing different stones under very good light. A sufficient selection of stones to determine which constitute heavily included stones and which do not will give you the clue. The stone you select will, no doubt, have a few needles. However, if this stone was properly oriented by the cutter, there should be no reflected needles visible through the table and hopefully not even through any part of the crown. If there are too many reflections (sheen) you may want to look for another stone. Since it is possible to find enough rhodolite garnet without too many flaws, a collector should be able to find suitable stones with just a little bit of shopping.

SPESSARTITE GARNET

SPESSARTITE GARNET: GENERAL COMMENTS

Acceptance with inclusions: Spessartite garnet is mostly considered a collector's gem. Production of fine spessartite gems has never been big. Spessartite is accorded some special allowances as regards inclusions. Eye clean stones do get produced in small quantities and bring a premium. Lightly to moderately included stones are still saleable however.

Size considerations: Large fine spessartite gems are quite rare. Spessartite never produces large gems like certain other silicates. Spessartite gems that are considered large do get by with a few more inclusions than smaller stones.

Color considerations: The finest colors of spessartite garnet are a bright orange color. Orange is not a dark color. As orange becomes darker it will generally due so by becoming more brown or more red--not premium colors for spessartite. Premium colors of spessartite do not conspire to hide inclusions. However, color is important enough that a particularly fine color will make a few inclusions acceptable.

Spessartite garnet, specific things to look for: Spessartite garnet, in spite of its sporadic availability, is so lovely and desirable it makes a worthwhile discussion. Spessartite occurs at various locations in the world, with some of the best stones coming from California and Virginia. The Ramona location in California still intermittently produces stones. Amelia Courthouse, the Virginia location, gives us stones only from old collections. Some also come from Brazil and Madagascar. The colors are quite lovely. The best and most desirable stones are vivid, bright, and quite pure orange for a natural stone. No absolutely clean orange stones of a really large size have come recently from any of the locations. However, there are rumors to the effect that bigger stones were available in the past. The orange stones we are speaking of come primarily from Ramona, California; one of the two gem garnet deposits in Brazil; and from Madagascar. This material has its primary problems with veil-type inclusions. In reality there are no inclusions in this material which are a problem for the collector since most of them are rather straightforward. However, it is necessary to distinguish inclusions in this material from the other color in which spessartite occurs.

The other color in which spessartite occurs is red-orange. While this color is equally attractive, it seldom comes in an absolutely clean stone. In spite of this fact, people seem to accept it because of its vibrant hue. Some of the choicest of this material is from Amelia Courthouse, Virginia. In examining these stones we have to look for veil-type inclusions of moderate grossness -- usually not quite as gross as the inclusions in the beryl family and usually not quite as fine as those in the andalusite material. The stone's rarity and interesting color helps in overlooking the fact that a completely clean stone is often not available. Yet, it is wise to exercise a great deal of caution in examining these gems. Examine the ones which are the least flawed, since, of course, they make the better choice.

It is usually quite easy to examine a spessartite for these veil-type inclusions. Since these stones are moderately dark, the inclusions may not stand out as prominently as in lighter stones. However, you will be able to find them and once you know where they are, you will be able to judge exactly how obtrusive they are. If you can find other stones of the same variety for comparison. If this is not possible judge the stone on brilliancy. Do the back facets reflect crisply and cleanly or are they fuzzy? If the stone has good clean brilliance, then the flaws are no problem and you have a good stone. If you are not sure and are not comfortable, then keep shopping.

PERIDOT

PERIDOT: GENERAL COMMENTS

Acceptance with inclusions: As a rule, peridot does not form with clean clear areas as clean and as clear as many other gems. Nevertheless, it has remarkable optical properties for a silicate gem. The high refractive index, strong birefringence and substantial dispersion create a gem that bedazzles the eye despite inclusions that would make other gem species look poorly. Peridot is a stone similar to andalusite in the sense that it is accepted despite inclusions that would not be acceptable in other gems.

Size considerations: While it is possible to buy peridot in substantial quantities at times most of the material is simply tumbling grade. Of the small amount of material that is facetable most of it is quite small. Large quantities of large peridot are just not available. Larger peridot stones can bring a premium despite inclusions.

Color considerations: Poor color peridot is so undesirable that virtually all peridot that is traded is halfway decent color. Within the range of color that is traded there is not a big enough a variation for the top color stones to make a difference in acceptability with flaws. The big range of color that exits, for instance with blue sapphire, just is not there with saleable peridot.

Peridot inclusions, specific things to look for: Peridot is unusual in terms of inclusions in that the two localities from which we are likely to get stones produce distinctly different types of inclusions. The most readily available source of small stones is Arizona. This material rarely comes with clean areas large enough to cut stones over three or four carats. Peridot from Arizona has what is in our experience a unique type of inclusion, referred to in the trade as a "lily pad" because it looks flat and round. This inclusion appears to be some kind of crystal which creates a space or small separation in the peridot which then gives a circular appearance which shines back when observed in a particular direction. Because of its flat and directional nature, "a la lily-pad," this inclusion is visible only when the breadth of the inclusion runs perpendicular to the light source. Therefore, when these stones are cut with the inclusions running perpendicular to the table, the cutter can effectively hide them. However, when these inclusions occur in too great a concentration, they are visible no matter how the stone is cut. Because of the difficulty of seeing these inclusions, many cutters have been disappointed by a clean appearing rough peridot, which was found to be flawed only after faceting. These flaws show up rather well under proper lightly. Since these are highly visible with proper lighting and are reflective in nature, use the same method of examining for these inclusions as you would for fractures in tsavorite or open cleavages in andalusite. In examining the stone to see these reflections it may be necessary to move the stone in the light in every conceivable direction. If you have done that and you do not find any inclusions, chances are you have a clean stone.

The other of the two world-wide localities producing gem-quality peridot are Burma and St. John's Island in the Red Sea. Burmese peridot can have biotite mica flake inclusions that are cloud-like in their overall spacing in the stone, and which are very small in size and brown in color. In many cases an apparently eye-clean stone from Burma will have these inclusions throughout the stone which are visible only by looking through a loupe. In other instances, a gem can be found that is nice in spite of having these inclusions. One should be very careful in buying Burmese peridot inasmuch as this inclusion can cause a very sleepy stone. Although much of peridot has sleepy characteristics anyway, adding the problems of these inclusions can, in some cases, result in a stone completely lacking in brilliance. Even though these inclusions are cloud-like, they occur in what can be roughly termed as planes.

QUARTZ GEMS

QUARTZ GEMS: GENERAL COMMENTS
(AMETHYST, CITRINE, AMETRINE)

Acceptance with inclusions: All varieties of quartz are so relatively common that the clarity standards are quite high for them with the notable exception of dark amethyst.

Size considerations: Virtually all color varieties of quartz produce fairly large gems in big quantities. None of the quartz gems gets a break for size.

Color considerations: Of the three quartz gems under examination here only dark, top color amethyst is accorded any laxity in clarity grading. The reason for this has to be at least in part due to the fact that certain inclusions can be well hidden by the dark color--especially if the inclusions are not near the surface of the stone. Of course another part of the reason is that there is no overwhelming production of super-fine dark amethyst. Sometimes we have to accept a few inclusions to get the best colored amethyst stones.

Quartz inclusions, specific things to look for: Luckily most faceted quartz gems that are traded in the market are fairly clean stones. One dealer will not buy them from another if they are not clean. There are no true challenges when it comes to buying most quartz gems. The two exceptions to this are citrine and dark amethyst. Citrine is a product of heat treating. The citrine color probably does exist in nature but virtually all gems on the market are heated along the way. This is known and accepted. The one thing to watch out for is the possibility of a heat fracture in the stone. Generally these are cut out of the rough during processing. However, once in awhile a stone can slip through the system harboring a fugitive fracture.

In the case of amethyst we can have a little more of a challenge. The very top color in amethyst will often occur in gems that have a few inclusions inside. Many times the inclusions are small enough or in little enough concentration so as not to hurt the gem's beauty. Perhaps a great danger here is for a potential buyer to be too strict. Truly fine Zambian amethyst can often have inclusions deep inside the stone that are eye visible with proper lighting. It takes a person with a fair amount of real, practical, grading knowledge to assess what is and what is not acceptable. A quick rule of thumb might be to look at the stone under normal conditions for long enough to feel comfortable that you do not see anything that mars its beauty. If you do find something, keep looking for another stone.

SPINEL

SPINEL: GENERAL COMMENTS

Acceptance with inclusions: Spinel is usually found in areas which also supply us with sapphire. Perhaps this has to do with the chemistry of both gems. Spinel is magnesium aluminum oxide while sapphire is aluminum oxide. The fact is that while spinel is associated with areas which produce sapphire, not all areas that produce sapphire also produce spinel. It seems that spinel is actually more rare than sapphire. While it is difficult to quantify rarity it is safe to say that spinel is one of the more rare gemstones. In addition to being a rare gem spinel is another of the gem minerals that does not produce large crystals. Taken together the rarity of spinel and the size of the crystals it produces force us to accept spinel with more inclusions than some other gems.

Size considerations: As mentioned above spinel does not come in huge crystals. Large cut stones of spinel are hard to get and coveted by collectors of rare gems. Larger cut stones of spinel are generally accepted with inclusions, sometimes even eye visible inclusions.

Color considerations: Color can be important to the value of spinel. The beautiful pink and red stones from Burma are the most sought after colors in spinel. When coupled with size, color can be a determining factor in accepting spinel gems with inclusions. Sometimes the color in a large spinel can be so dazzling that a gem with eye visible inclusions is wonderfully beautiful despite the inclusions. Remember, beauty is the rule that overrules all others.

Spinel inclusions, specific things to look for: The inclusions in spinel are usually pretty straightforward. However, one of the most common spinel inclusions which may give problems at times are included crystals. In some spinel the included crystals are very small, polite and cause no trouble whatsoever. At other times, spinel has crystal inclusions which causes separation in the spinel itself. The separation is probably caused by the two different minerals, the spinel and the included crystals, which have different coefficients of expansion. During the formation of spinel there is certainly a great deal of heat. After formation and during the cooling process, the spinel presumably cooled faster and shrank more than the included crystal. The circular nature of the crack or separation gives it the halo appearance noted by gemologists. While these cracks virtually never make the spinel fragile, the halo can often reflect light like any other type of crack or cleavage. If the reflecting light is too obvious or too many of such inclusions appear, a stone can be ruined. Some of these halos can be seen from any angle, while others can be found only after a great deal of study. Simply looking at the stone with reflected light, as in a jewelry mounting, is the technique. Look at the stone from all angles in this manner to see if there is a halo. If there is, and it spoils the appearance of the stone, you may not want to buy it. If, on the other hand, this shiny, little halo is small and the stone is remarkable in all other ways, you may want to buy.

SPODUMENE

SPODUMENE (VARIETY, KUNZITE): GENERAL COMMENTS

Acceptance with inclusions: Kunzite falls into the category of stones like aquamarine and citrine. It should be free of eye visible inclusions.

Size considerations: Kunzite again falls into the same category as aquamarine. Size really makes no difference. Kunzite crystals can occur in some of the largest cleanest gem crystals ever seen.

Color considerations: Color does not seem to make much difference in accepting kunzite with inclusions. While it is nice to have a top color kunzite gem, it really does not make inclusions any more acceptable.

Kunzite inclusions, specific things to look for: Kunzite, while being very difficult to cut in respect to its cleavages and resistance in grinding, also has problems in the form of tubular inclusions which, in some cases, are not immediately observable. These tubular inclusions virtually always run parallel to the "C" axis for awhile and then veer off in another direction, usually in response to some change in the crystal itself. Since most spodumene has a highly striated exterior in the rough, these tubular inclusions can be very difficult to find. This is another case where a cutter may leave an inclusion in a stone inadvertently. Fortunately, these tubes in the finished stone are not too terribly difficult to spot. Kunzite is almost never too dark to preclude an easy examination. The difficulty here comes in the orientation of the inclusion. The tubular inclusions are invariably perpendicular to the table of the cut stone for two reasons. The first reason for cutting this way is to obtain the proper color orientation for kunzite, which is perpendicular to the "C" crystal axis and even clean stones are cut this way. Secondly, having the tubes perpendicular to the table tends to hide them. When you look down on the table, you will be looking at the tubes on end and you may or may not perceive them. Sometimes a particularly good colored kunzite might have a couple of these inclusions. Depending upon the number of them and their size, they may or may not be made up for by the color. Since kunzite of especially fine color is very rare, do not be discouraged by the existence of these inclusions if they are minor in proportion.

Since spodumene cleaves in two directions, open cleavages are another problem for the collector to watch for in this gem. Looking for open cleavages in kunzite is just like looking for open cleavages in andalusite or fractures in grossular garnet. The minute parting between the two planes interferes with light in such a way as to cause reflection. Again, since the reflection will only occur on the plane it may be difficult to spot. By continually rotating the stone in every direction you will eventually find an angle where the incidence of light against the plane will reflect the light back into your eye. The open cleavage will appear to you in the form of reflection that does not belong. Once you find it, look at it even more carefully. Since the cleavages in kunzite once started can continue to open, it is best to refrain from buying kunzite which has open cleavages whatsoever.

IMPERIAL AND PINK TOPAZ

IMPERIAL AND PINK TOPAZ: GENERAL COMMENTS

Acceptance with inclusions: If you ever saw a piece of imperial topaz gem rough you might expect to only see very included cut stones. The fact that there are eye clean gems available in the marketplace is testimony to the hard work and skill of gem cutters in Brazil. The fact is that both pink and imperial topaz are expected to be eye clean.

Size considerations: In most instances size exerts no influence on the basic requirement of pink and imperial topaz to be eye clean. However, truly large stones over 20 carats are not that easy to obtain. Speaking personally, if given the choice between an eye clean stone of 4 carats and a truly nice gem of 20 carats with a small visible inclusion off in one corner of the stone I'd say--go for the big one.

Color considerations: Color can play a huge factor in the price of imperial and pink topaz. In the case of an imperial topaz with a deep pinkish red color or a pink topaz with a deep hot pink color a few inclusions might be forgiven. The inclusions might bring the price down as compared with a similar stone without inclusions. When combined with unusual size, fine color could be influential in the acceptance of minor eye visible inclusions.

Imperial and pink topaz inclusions, specific things to look for: Another pegmatite material, like beryl and kunzite, we include in our list is topaz. Pink and Imperial topaz have three types of problems of which the collector must be aware. First of all, as you will find in the properties listed in the photo chapter, topaz has what is referred to as perfect cleavage. While this cleavage is nothing to worry about normally, open cleavages should not be present in any finished stones. The problem represented by cleavage is only a problem once it has started to open up, much like a tear in a garment. Once it starts, it tends to continue. Starting the tear may be difficult, but continuing afterward is relatively easy. To examine Imperial topaz for open cleavages, use the same method as for kunzite. Any open cleavage will look like a shiny spot which does not belong.

Cracks are a second problem for topaz. Although these are rarely found in finished stones, they occur frequently in rough crystals. There is always an off chance that a cutter might leave one in. Cracks look much like open cleavages and can be found using the same process. The difference between the two inclusions will be their orientation in the crystal and therefore the stone. The difference is more academic than pragmatic and does not matter to the collector. Just be aware that they might be in a topaz.

Perhaps the most tricky inclusions to look for in topaz are tubular inclusions. They occur only rarely and are very fine and difficult to spot. Finding them requires much the same technique as finding cracks or open cleavages, so you can look for all three at the same time. Be sure to remember that they are difficult to find, thus if they are too difficult to find it may make no difference that they are there and a stone may be okay with these inclusions.

TOURMALINE

In dealing with tourmaline we will deal with blue tourmaline, green tourmaline, pink tourmaline, and rubellite separately.

BLUE TOURMALINE: GENERAL COMMENTS

Acceptance with inclusions: Blue tourmaline ranks with rubellite as one of the more rare colors of tourmaline. Most blue tourmaline forms in crystals which are fairly clean. Despite its rarity blue tourmaline is expected to be relatively free from flaws.

Size considerations: Blue tourmaline generally does not come in large cut stones. Many times if blue tourmaline does come in a large stone the result will be a gem that is too dark. For that reason the gem is often then heat treated to lighten the piece. Most of these gems then turn into a very fine green tourmaline. Large, fine blue tourmaline gems are quite rare and unusual. These gems are rare enough that it is difficult to say what the "market" has in mind for them. There is no "market" in something that rare. Our guess is that a few inclusions might be accepted in a blue tourmaline if it were of a size to be considered unusual.

Color considerations: Very fine color in a blue tourmaline can create a lot of extra demand for the stone. Some of the now famous gems from the Paraiba mining district in Brazil brought sums into the thousands of dollars per-carat. Some of the lesser grade gems had inclusions in them and were bought and sold at prices in the hundreds of dollars per-carat due to the fine color but despite the inclusions. So the answer in the case of color for green tourmaline: yes color can bend the rule for eye clean gems in the case of blue tourmaline. If you are wondering why we're speaking of Paraiba tourmaline in the past tense, the mines from that area produced gems for a short time and as of this writing are no longer producing.

GREEN TOURMALINE: GENERAL COMMENTS

Acceptance with inclusions: As a rule green tourmaline should be eye clean.

Size considerations: In the stones we've seen to date size has no impact on whether or not a green tourmaline should be accepted with inclusions.

Color considerations: With the exception of some green Paraiba tourmaline we've never seen tourmaline get a break with regards to inclusions based on color. Some of the green tourmaline from the Paraiba district were saleable despite the accompaniment of inclusions. However, even these stones were not accorded the same acceptability mentioned above for the blue stones.

Blue and Green Tourmaline

Blue and green tourmaline: specific things to look for: One of the most varietal of all gemstones is tourmaline, a pegmatitic mineral like topaz, spodumene, and beryl. Tourmaline that is available on the market may be categorized in three varieties: blue and green found in single crystal form; pink and rubellite found in single crystals; and pink and rubellite found in multiple crystal growths. Although these categories are based on crystal appearance, they do have specific types of inclusions which are of consequence to the collector.

The blue and green varieties notably have fractures circling the periphery of the crystal. Blue and green tourmaline varieties are highly dichroic with the number two color being so dark down the "C" axis that it is nearly always impossible to look into the stone to see how deep the peripheral fractures run into the stone. Even in the best of rough material, small fractures are found in the outer rind of the crystal. Sometimes the fractures go all the way into the stone and a parting can occur at this place. If the cutter has overlooked this break point you could be purchasing a stone which, although rare, could crack. Looking for a crack in this type of tourmaline is much like looking for a cleavage. Since these cracks are found on the outer rind of the rough crystal, they tend to appear in the periphery of a cut stone. If there are any cracks they will appear as a line or a ring around the stone. The ring may be broken if part of the crack has been ground away. However, a collector wants to avoid even such a small remnant if possible. There are exceptions. If the crack is truly small and the stone is truly remarkable in every other way it may be worth owning.

PINK TOURMALINE: GENERAL COMMENTS

Acceptance with inclusions: With the exception of the pink tourmaline that comes from rubellite-type crystals, pink tourmaline is expected to be eye-clean. Pink tourmaline that comes from rubellite-type crystals exhibits an intense hot-pink color that is worth the price of a few small inclusions.

Size considerations: Again we come to the dichotomy of those pink tourmaline stones that are from crystals formed along the lines of green tourmaline and those formed along the lines of rubellite. In the case of the former the gems are expected to be eye-clean whatever the size while the latter are forgiven some inclusions no matter the size.

Color considerations: As mentioned above the pink color that comes in rubellite-type crystals is accepted with a certain amount of eye-visible inclusions.

PINK AND RUBELLITE TOURMALINE -- SINGLE CRYSTAL

Pink tourmaline: specific things to look for: Pink and rubellite tourmaline of the single crystal variety resemble the blue and green variety since they are from the same crystal structure. However, there is a difference found by looking down the "C" axis of this stone. Sometimes when looking down the "C" axis of Mozambique tourmalines there is a rind of one color pink and a center color of another pink, and the pattern made of the two colors looks like the letter "Y". If a piece looks as though it has all of these features, it may be an unstable gemstone. Look for this by simply holding the stone so that you have light coming through the end of the stone. This is done by putting the tip of one end of the stone at the lip of the high intensity light and looking into the other end of the stone, while making sure not to look into the light source. In most cases, cutters avoid this type of stone because it can crack during the cutting procedure. However, if you find one which as been successfully faceted it might be a problem at some later date and is possibly a good stone to avoid.

Pink and Rubellite Tourmaline -- Multiple Crystal*

Specific things to look for: The most stable variety of tourmaline, although frequently flawed, is pink and rubellite tourmaline in multiple crystal form. This type of rubellite crystal has the very best color, but with a certain amount of inclusions. Typical rubellite inclusions are tubular and veil type inclusions. Interestingly, rubellites sell for several hundred dollars per carat when they have the best color, despite having inclusions. The inclusions most common in this type of tourmaline are veils, tubes and needles. These stones hold together more easily in cutting, polishing and wearing than stones of the single crystal variety. Be aware when buying multiple crystal tourmalines, because there will be a few inclusions in the stone. If the color of the finished stone is good enough, these stones are accepted and can be enjoyed.

To distinguish multiple crystal tourmaline from single crystal tourmaline look at all the rubellite you can find from all available sources. After you have done a great deal of looking, you will be able to distinguish between a multiple crystal tourmaline and the single crystal variety, no matter what the exact color. Since many dealers themselves do not know the exact crystal

*We are calling this type of crystal in which rubellite is found "multiple-crystal" since it looks like a bunch of smaller crystals bundled together. Minerologists may cringe at this usage. However, we need to distinguish our observations through useful descriptions.

difference, it is best to start this process with rubellite and generalize later into pink. It is simply a matter of experience.

ZOISITE

ZOISITE (VARIETY TANZANITE): GENERAL COMMENTS

Acceptance with inclusions: Tanzanite is generally expected to come in eye-clean gems. This may change in future years as the mine plays out.

Size considerations: Larger tanzanite is definitely more expensive per-carat up to the 10 carat mark. However, eye-visible inclusions are still not accepted.

Color considerations: Tanzanite is still new enough to the gem world that color preference is not as rigid as with sapphire or ruby. For this reason no particular color can carry the burden of extra inclusions.

Zoisite/tanzanite specific things to look for: The variety of zoisite most familiar to everyone is tanzanite. Tanzanite currently commands very high prices in finished stones. While most of the problem inclusions in tanzanite are on the outer rind and cut away during the lapidary process, there are a couple of problems to watch for in finished stones. The most common of these two uncommon problems is the inclusion of needle-like rutile. Sometimes these needles come right down the center of a perfectly clean stone, thereby causing a stone, which otherwise might be worth several thousand dollars, to become relatively worthless. Small rutile needles off to the side of an otherwise fine stone can be accepted if they're unobtrusive. While they are not that common in tanzanite, they are not difficult to find. The main problem is knowing to look for them in the first place and remembering to do so when examining tanzanite before purchase.

A second problem, and very much less common in tanzanite, is twinning. Twinning can be described as either the natural joining of two crystals, or as a situation where a crystal stopped growing and then began to grow again, with the new growth in the form of a somewhat discreet crystal. Usually the twinning occurs along a plane. Although a twinning plane in tanzanite may not be weak, it will usually interfere to a certain extent with the play of light and therefore the stone may not be desirable. Twinning planes are almost always very subtle and difficult to find. A twinning plane which is well put together simply looks like a dark phantom in the stone and there is no good recipe for finding it other than intense looking. By contrast, a twinning plane which has a weak bond may appear as a crack or a cleavage and may reflect light and be easier to find using the same technique for finding open cleavages. Again, while this type of inclusion is very unusual in tanzanite, it is one of those inclusions which does occur from time to time in this gemstone.

CONCLUSION

In concluding this chapter on problem inclusions in finished gemstones we want to re-emphasize some of the points we have made. First, be aware of which types of inclusions are found in which gem varieties. Second, get to know their relative importance to the value of that stone as a collector. Third, know how to look for these inclusions, even the more difficult ones. Finally, use this chapter to assist you in your search for the best possible stone for the money when you are buying.

VII

TREATED STONES

The average retail jewelry buyer seldom hears anything about the subject of this chapter. Yet as soon as a person enters the world of gemstones in a serious way as a collector, one of the first things they hear about is treated stones. Unfortunately many times the first words one hears about treated stones are distortions of the real facts or a few scattered truths not put into their proper place or perspective. As a collector it is important that you know enough about this subject to help make proper purchases and not become confused.

These remarks are directed to the relative newcomers to the gemology field to acquaint them with various types of treated stones and types of treatments which we find in today's marketplace.

WHAT IS A TREATED STONE?

The first step in understanding and being able to discuss treated gems is to define what constitutes a treated stone. A treated gem usually starts as a stone which, from the mine, has an inferior color that can be

165

improved by applying different forms of energy, such as heat or radiation and/or the use of chemicals in conjunction with such energies. Treated stones are different from other types of gemstones in that there is an additional step between the mining process and purchase by the final consumer.

So, What's the Problem?

In a sense, the treating of stones has always been looked at somewhat askance because the value of gemstones has always been based, for the most part, upon intrinsic value. Intrinsic value is the value an object has in and of itself. When you alter the substance, the questions arise: "Does that particular substance continue to have intrinsic value after being changed?" Or, "is it possible to create intrinsic value?" Such questions are at the root of why people pay high prices for small amounts of substances. However, since the market has dealt with the question of treated gemstones for quite some time, it seems that the market has been answering those questions right along. Such important questions are raised by the existence of treated gemstones and we feel it necessary that the collector be aware of treated gemstones as part of his education.

In earlier times the treatment of gemstones was either so crude that the treatment was easily detected and the value of the stone discounted, or the treatment created such a minor change in the stone that the change, although noticeable, was scientifically undetectable and therefore accepted. The market was not confronted with any great dilemmas as to accepting or not accepting, buying or not buying treated gems. However, currently there are such sophisticated treatments that the marketplace needs a continuous updating.

For instance, until approximately 35 years ago it would have been unthinkable to take an opaque, extremely dark gem and turn it into a transparent gem of substantially lighter color. Such treatment is currently going on in some gem species and it is well for everyone in the market to know the extent to which gem materials can be physically changed.

We are not going to talk about outdated techniques, or tried-a-few-times techniques, but rather talk about treatments which can be accurately described, and which can be found in gems currently in the marketplace.

A newcomer to the gem market often hears conflicting bits of information, many times from spurious sources. We like to compare the gemstone world of the beginner to that of a person walking into a movie halfway through. No one is around to tell him the plot. People who know a little say something which may contain a kernel of truth. They then add to that kernel pieces of information containing little or no truth at all. What happens? Many myths and rumors come into existence and are perpetuated. But gemology is a science -- there is no room for myth.

WHAT IS ACCEPTABLE?

Right at the start we want to clear up the myth that dealing in treated stones is unethical. This simply is not so. We do not have a particular fondness for certain treated gems, but treated gems have enjoyed a niche in the past, and continue to enjoy one in the present marketplace. Your job, as the potential collector of gemstones, lies in knowing what the market considers acceptable treated gemstones and which treated gemstones are considered unacceptable.

Gemstones are treated for three reasons. First, because the supply of stones has dwindled. Centuries of production are playing out existing mines. Second, our modern times of great international wealth creates a demand for all types of gem material. Third, technology, especially that which did not exist several years ago, has finally filtered into the gem field.

There are two important facts you must know if you are to deal with the question of treated stones successfully. The first fact is that certain treated stones are acceptable in the marketplace and command both high prices and respect. The second is that certain other treated stones are not worth buying, and selling these stones must be looked on as a dubious practice. Because of this difference, we want to give a brief description of terms to clarify our last statement.

When we use the term acceptable, we mean that the gem trade accepts a particular stone in its treated form as not having a diminished value. Why certain treatments of certain stones are accepted and others are not is a subject that has not been widely discussed in print. It seems that every gem expert has his own pet theory to resolve the acceptability question. However, even more important than the theories of experts are the dictates of the market. In the final analysis the market is boss. Within the market one common denominator seems to exist: acceptance of treated stones where the treatment and the final product simulate nature. For example, the market accepts blue topaz. Blue topaz occurs in nature and the treatment method simulates nature's method of coloring blue topaz. In most instances where the treatment method and the final product simulate nature it becomes virtually impossible to detect treated from untreated stones. The market resolves this problem by adjusting the price for the particular variety of gem to encompass all available gems -- both treated and untreated. Fortunately for the gem market, the natural raw material for treating gems is usually itself somewhat scarce and that portion which produces fine quality treated stones even rarer.

The term "unacceptable" applies when the market decides that the treatment method and its products do not deserve a place in the market. Most unacceptable treatment methods alter the physical makeup of the stone in an easily recognizable way. Usually the method is recognizable due to it's crudity or because the alteration does not produce a product simulating a naturally occurring gem. Another type of unacceptable treatment happens when the resulting color is impermanent. You would not want to buy a vibrantly colored stone today only to have it lose 90% of its color tomorrow. We also want to mention that treating stones for the primary purpose of defrauding the public obviously falls into the unacceptable category.

OUR PLAN OF ACTION

We are going to discuss four well-known treatment methods -- heat treatment; heat and chemical treatment; radiation treatment; and heat and radiation treatment. Each method is applied to certain stones to achieve a particular desired result. Hopefully, our discussion will leave you with a precise idea of what these treatments involve, which stones they apply to, and what results the trade tries to achieve by use of each specific method. Most importantly, we will tell you which treatments are acceptable or unacceptable and why or why not.

HEAT TREATMENT

The first method of treatment we would like to discuss is heat treatment. Heat treatment involves raising the temperature of a stone until it changes color. For the most part heat treated stones are accepted in the marketplace because virtually all of them are permanent in color after treating.

Tourmaline, aquamarine, citrine, tanzanite, and Imperial topaz are stones which achieve permanent color through heat treatment and are accepted by the trade.

At this point we would like to discuss individual gem varieties and discuss them specifically in regard to heat treating. Lets begin with tourmaline.

TOURMALINE

In both green and blue tourmaline the original color from the mine is often too dark to produce an attractive stone and can sometimes be lightened by heat treating. The success of heat treating this type of tourmaline varies from one mining area to another and, in fact, from mine to mine. The gems from certain mines tend to respond to heat treatment and in other instances they do not. The origin of the stone can even become so specific that gems from certain areas of certain mines will treat while others will not. Virtually every Brazilian gem dealer in the tourmaline-producing areas of Brazil has a kiln for heat treating green tourmaline. The pink and rubellite colors of tourmaline are treated less frequently. Heating pink tourmaline and rubellite tourmaline sometimes drives off brown overtones and lightens its general color as well.

The process for heat treating tourmaline is very simple. In most cases the rough gem is ground to remove any inclusions or existing cracks as these can cause the entire stone to split apart. After this process the stone is simply heated. Some people put the tourmalines into sand to insulate it from a too rapid temperature change but others do not bother with this step. The upper range for heating tourmalines in a normal atmosphere is approximately 700°C (approx. 1,285°F). Beyond that temperature tourmaline will de-gas and be completely ruined. Since this is so common a practice, one has to wonder if tourmalines having a naturally good color might not have undergone such a treatment in nature. Heat treated tourmaline is considered an acceptable product.

AQUAMARINE

Almost all of the beryl sold as aquamarine in the market starts its trip from the mine as a green beryl. In aquamarine, heat treatment drives off the yellow component of the green hue and produces a lively sky blue color. Aquamarine has the distinction of being the most popular heat treated gemstone in the trade. No doubt, the long-term acceptance of aquamarine paves the way for acceptability of that treatment in other gems simply because of its prevalence in aquamarine and the popularity of aquamarine itself.

The treatment method for aquamarine is very similar to that of tourmaline. However, since beryl has very little heat sensitivity the precaution of heating it within an insulation medium is rarely observed. The temperatures achieved in heat treating aquamarine range anywhere from 300°C to 500°C (approx. 575°F-925°F). Heat treated aquamarine is fully accepted by the market.

CITRINE

The gem ranking first in number of carats treated is citrine. Most citrine begins its existence as low to medium grade amethyst. The stones are heated after cobbing the crystals to remove included areas. The purple of the amethyst disappears, and the golden brown of citrine remains. The dramatic change of purple to golden yellow and orange can be very stunning.

Since the amethyst that turns into citrine changes color with relatively little energy input, the temperature at which it is treated is relatively low, probably somewhere in the 95°C-125°C (approx. 200°F-250°F) range. Heat treated citrine is accepted by the market.

TANZANITE

If the change of citrine from purple to gold and orange is dramatic, perhaps equally dramatic is the change due to heat treating tanzanite. We think the gemstone tanzanite presents an interesting case because when first faceted its original color is very unattractive. We have heard this color described as lizard skin blue/purple/brown. Some "purists" in the collecting community used to ask for an untreated tanzanite and when they saw how ugly it is, changed their order in favor of a treated stone. Heating tanzanite drives off the brown and leaves a stone which, in some cases, rivals the best Ceylon sapphire blue.

The heat used to treat tanzanite is somewhere between that used for aquamarine and tourmaline, about 450°C-600°C (approx. 850°F-1100°F). Tanzanite must be heat treated with the utmost care because tanzanite is very susceptible to thermal shock. While it can be taken up to relatively high temperatures, it must be taken there slowly. It cannot be steam cleaned because of the rapid temperature change, but can be heated to higher temperatures in a kiln, if heated very slowly. Tanzanite is an acceptable heat treated gem.

IMPERIAL TOPAZ

It has been documented that certain Imperial topazes will respond to heat treatment. As long ago as the early 1970's it was rumored that certain of the fancy colors in Imperial topaz were aided by the treatment. In the early 1980's some scholarly research concluded that it is possible to modify the color of some Imperial topaz through heat treatment. However, to date, knowledge regarding this material remains somewhat sketchy. The red, red-pink and pink colors are thought to be improved with this process. However, it seems that while this treatment is a possibility, current practice sees little or none of it happening commercially. Pakistan produces a precious pink topaz and little or no orange material. The mines in Ouro Preto, Brazil, all produce a range of colors going from yellow to gold to orange to pink, and finally red. The rough, uncut material, seen for sale at the mines has this color range. The same range of colors, in corresponding quantities, is seen in the cut stones in neighboring cities. This correspondence of color range in rough and cut stones plus the premium prices paid for the pink-red end of the spectrum indicate that there is no significant commercial heat treatment of this material. It has been hypothesized that if there is any treatment being done that the stones which respond are so few and the dollar gamble so high that this is not a widespread practice. In any case, while this is a matter for the collector to be aware of, it has not affected the market price of this lovely material. Whatever amount of this imperial/pink topaz that is heat treated is obviously accepted by the market.

HEAT AND CHEMICAL TREATMENT

The next method of treatment we want to address is that using heat and chemicals combined to achieve a desired result. We have learned from study and observation that this process attempts to simulate a crystal's natural growing environment. The aim seems to be to aid the crystal in reconstructing itself under conditions better than the original ones under which the stone was formed. In turn, this produces a purer crystal, more salable to the marketplace.

Acceptability of stones treated by this method varies. Australian sapphire, Ceylon sapphire, and rubies, all members of the corundum family, are generally accepted and their final color is permanent. There are exceptions.

Blue zircon, although also accepted, has color which can only be said to be substantially permanent.

AUSTRALIAN SAPPHIRES

The treatment of Australian sapphires with heat and chemicals starts with stones which are rather opaque and extremely dark in color. The stone is heated in oxidizing chemicals to the melting point. The effect is to drive off the overly dark blue color and produce a stone of a lighter shade of blue.

The end result is a facetable piece of rough which is quite marketable, although still bringing lower prices than sapphires from other places.

CEYLON SAPPHIRE

In terms of color, treating Ceylon sapphire takes an opposite viewpoint -- taking a light colored stone and intensifying or darkening its original color. After heating the stone to the melting point in a particular chemical environment, we have a stone of a rather nice medium to intense blue shade.

The interesting fact about the current treatment of the Ceylon sapphire with this method is that those stones which are accepted in the marketplace start out as a milky white crystal. These stones go by the name "geuda."

Ceylon sapphires treated by this method are accepted in the trade.

RUBY

Ruby is treated with heat and oxidizing chemicals. The heat tends to dissolve rutile inclusions that might make the stones have a sleepy or fuzzy appearance. The oxygen tends to drive off purple hues and leave this stone a nice red color. Rubies treated by this method are the norm. Non-treated documentation can command a premium.

THE DIFFUSION METHOD OF TREATING SAPPHIRES

There is another type of sapphire, mostly Ceylon sapphire, treated with heat and chemicals but which are of a different crystal make up than the Ceylon sapphires we talked about before. It is very important to make this distinction -- one treatment from the other. This treatment starts with pale to colorless Ceylon sapphires. This particular method of heat and chemical treatment creates a change in color which penetrates the stone, usually cut stones, to a depth of perhaps a few microns up to 1/2 millimeter. When these stones are submerged in a liquid of high enough refractive index, such as methylene iodide, they tend to look like a shell. The colored area is like an eggshell around a yolk of white. These stones are currently a matter of some controversy in the gem trade. We have to wonder, in stones of sufficiently small size, where the penetration of the chemical goes to the center of the stone, if it would be possible to distinguish these from stones which are natural or from stones treated with another method. This is the latest technique in the treatment of sapphires, and the exact reaction of the market to this seems to be undecided at the current time.

ZIRCON

Zircon is the next stone up for discussion. You may find it interesting that the method of treating zircon is an ancient one in Southeast Asia. The treatment results in a change in color from brown to a vivid blue. The method uses heat plus chemicals that create a reducing atmosphere.

Unfortunately, this color is only substantially permanent; by which we mean it loses color over an extended period of time. As a buyer you need not be concerned, because this period of time is very long. There are estate pieces which are decades old in which if there are color changes they are negligible.

RADIATION TREATMENT

From heat and chemical treatment we would like to move on to radiation treatment. It is a method we find particularly difficult to describe because there are many different methods of radiation used in treating stones. However, we can say that gems treated with radiation have variable color permanency from variety to variety and some of the varieties being treated by this method are still under development, so their acceptability has not been firmly determined.

KUNZITE

Kunzite is a gem which some people have treated experimentally with irradiation. Natural kunzite comes in a range of color from light pink through hot pink into a medium lavender. This gemstone is another spodumene with variable color permanency when treated and whose process of treatment through radiation is still under development. The reports about treatment of this stone vary. We have heard of successes in enhancing the color with good color stability and we have heard reports of rapid color loss. No doubt, both of these statements have some truth in them. Kunzite comes from a multiple of sites in the world, and even natural kunzite loses its color over the years if put in sunlight.

MORGANITE/HALBANITE

In the 1970's a new aquamarine rival came out of Brazil. This stone was named Halbanite. Halbanite, or Halbanita as it is called in Brazil, is a peculiar form of morganite which can be treated from a pale pinkish color into a deep aquamarine blue. The treatment process involves the use of short wave ultraviolet light. The radiant energy of ultraviolet waves changes this particular morganite's color. It was determined within a few months after discovery that the blue in Halbanite is unstable in sunlight and will fade quickly. Since this material is a natural beryl it might be more difficult for some people to distinguish from aquamarine than a substitute stone. However, it looks somewhat different than a true aqua and can be distinguished by several gemological tests. Since this material has the unhappy habit of fading rapidly in direct sunlight, Halbanite is an unacceptable treated stone.

IMPERIAL TOPAZ

In the late 1970's and early 1980's the colored stone business was shaken by the irradiation of Imperial topaz. Treating Imperial topaz with radiation evolved as a natural offshoot of the work done treating blue topaz, a stone known to most gem collectors. Unlike blue topaz's treatment, however, this method does not involve heating of the stones after irradiation. What shook up the gem business was the adverse reaction of Imperial topaz to radiation and the possibility of creating a glut of this material on the market.

Imperial topaz has an adverse reaction to radiation in that the resultant color is impermanent. It is true that some yellow Imperial topaz can be enhanced into deeper more orange looking color. However these stones become an insipid yellow after only a short exposure to sunlight. For this reason, irradiated Imperial topaz is an unacceptable product. Fortunately this product had a poor reception on the market and the ease of detection has kept this item from being produced on a wide scale. Interestingly enough, pink or pink-red topaz apparently cannot be produced by irradiation so these premium colors should be free from suspicion. As the scientific truth involved in this matter came to light the original shake-up of the late 70's and early 80's began to subside.

RUBELLITE

Irradiation of rubellite on a commercial basis is one of the latest uses of this treatment technique. One of the early problems with irradiated rubellite was the addition of a brown color component that rendered the stones unattractive and readily discernible from their untreated counterparts. However, in later years this problem was overcome and a certain percentage of irradiated rubellites began to look quite attractive.

The advent of commercially irradiating rubellite with a successful appearance is new enough that the effect on the rubellite market is hard to determine. In our opinion the raw material for treating into rubellite is itself fairly rare so the supply should never glut the market as did blue topaz. Currently, it is assumed that most rubellite is irradiated whether it is or not. This fact does not seem to affect the market price.

DIAMONDS

Last but not least, we want to discuss the irradiation of diamonds. In a general sense, the irradiation treatment of diamonds involves more than just radiation. However, it has been brought to our attention that a certain amount of experimentation is being done with simple radiation involving different sources of radiation than the traditional methods originally discovered many years ago. Just what the sources of radiation are, the energies used, and success of these treatments remains unknown inasmuch as such experiments are highly secret. However, we have learned that such treatment is being used experimentally and it will be worth keeping an ear to the ground to hear if such a treatment method becomes prevalent.

RADIATION AND HEAT TREATMENT

The final form of treatment in our discussion is the use of radiation and heat. Certainly the best known product to undergo this treatment is blue topaz. This gem is accepted widely in the trade and has a permanent color. As you may know, blue topaz does occur naturally. However, nearly all the material we see offered in the current market has been treated.

The specific method of using radiation and heat in the treatment of blue topaz is to first subject the gems to radiation of perhaps various sorts and intensities, after which the gem is rendered a smokey color, much like smokey quartz. After the gem has been irradiated to that color, it is then subjected to heat in an oven in a temperature range of 95°C-200°C (approx. 200°F-400°F). This drives off the smokey color and leaves the blue color. It seems a somewhat involved process, but it is quite successful and relatively inexpensive. There are other more involved treatments as well. However going into each and every treatment for blue topaz is beyond the scope of this book.

This gemstone has become a modern favorite due to its beauty, permanence of color and relatively reasonable prices.

There has been some dispute as to the color permanence of irradiated blue topaz and some people may doubt that the color is permanent. In terms of heat, heat itself can cause fading of blue topaz, but the stone must be subjected to temperatures in excess of 200°C (approx. 400°F), which certainly would not happen under normal circumstances of jewelry use. Another method of fading this material would be to subject it to a sufficient amount of ultraviolet radiation. However, the amount of ultraviolet radiation necessary to be equal in energy to a 200°C(approx. 400°F) oven is so enormous as to not exist naturally in the form of sunlight. In regard to this dispute, we would definitely say blue topaz has color permanency. Permanency certainly adequate for any reasonable jewelry use.

DIAMONDS

As a fitting finale we have diamonds. Diamonds can be considered special in the subject of treatment because they were one of the first commercially successful radiation projects in gemstones. Certainly the high value of diamonds and the importance of color to the price of diamonds makes them a natural target for irradiation experiments. In the case of diamonds we are talking about treating gems into the so-called fancy colors. In the diamond trade stones of bright vivid yellow, blue, pink, green, and even brown are called "fancies." Irradiation and heat can turn straw yellow, gray and milky brown into vivid hues. Fortunately, a great deal of research has been done to enable distinctions to be made relatively easily between natural and induced colors in diamonds. Irradiated diamonds are accepted by the trade and the colors are considered permanent. The extensive treatment of diamonds through radiation and heat has created a market and a market price for those stones.

The treatment of diamonds involves radiation with a cyclotron, after which the diamonds are subjected to heat in an oven with a special atmosphere. Apparently it is necessary to increase the temperature of the diamonds after radiation to the temperatures at which they would actually burn. Since diamonds are carbon and would oxidize, the special atmosphere in the oven prevents oxidization from taking place and permits the final steps in artificially coloring diamonds.

SUMMARY

No doubt, there are other stones on the market we could have included in this chapter. However, the purpose of this chapter was to introduce you to the world of treated stones. We hope we have given you a beginning basis of facts about treated stones which will serve as a springboard to further education as you explore the field of gemstones and gemstone collecting. For a more detailed eduction in this field, the GIA colored stone course is the best bet.

VIII

GEM COLLECTOR REFERENCE

NAME OF GEMSTONE:
Andalusite
(aluminum silicate)
Variety: Andalusite
Color Occurrences: *andalusite*
brownish green
reddish brown
brownish red

OPTICAL AND PHYSICAL PROPERTIES:
Refractive Indices:
1.634-1.643 ± .005

Birefringence: .008 to .013
Pleochroism: trichroic, strong
Dispersion: .016
Specific Gravity: 3.13-3.21; 3.17 normal

JEWELRY PROPERTIES:
Hardness: 7-71/2
Cleavage: distinct
Fracture: uneven
Toughness: fair to good
Steam Cleaning: better not to steam clean

IMPORTANT SIZE: over 2 carats; fine quality stones over 5 carats are difficult to find.

CURRENT COMMERCIALLY IMPORTANT LOCATIONS: Brazil; Sri Lanka.

COMMENTS: Andalusite -- Andalusite is a lovely trichroic stone. That is to say, part of its beauty is the three colors it exhibits. Andalusite is not well enough known and the trichroism makes its appearance so variable that market preference is not as strongly defined as with other stones.

186

NAME OF GEMSTONE:

Beryl
(silicate of aluminum & beryllium)
Variety: Aquamarine
Color Occurrences: *aquamarine*
Aquamarine is pale to medium sea green, sky blue or grayish blue.

OPTICAL AND PHYSICAL PROPERTIES:

Refractive Indices: 1.577-1.583 ± 0.17
Birefringence: .005 to .009, weak
Pleochroism: Aquamarine - dichroic strong to weak

Dispersion: .014, medium
Specific Gravity: 2.67-2.84; 2.72 normal

JEWELRY PROPERTIES:

Hardness: 7 1/2-8
Cleavage: very difficult; one direction
Fracture: tough to uneven, conchoidal
Toughness: Aquamarine -- fair to good, often brittle.
Steam Cleaning: Aquamarine -- not recommended

IMPORTANT SIZE: Aquamarine -- over 5 carats; fine quality stones are available up to several hundred carats.

CURRENT COMMERCIALLY IMPORTANT LOCATIONS: Aquamarine -- Brazil; India, Nigeria; Kenya; Afghanistan.

COMMENTS: Aquamarine is a surprising stone once you get to know it. Gems with substantial color can bring hundreds of dollars per-carat even on the wholesale level. Since the demand for fine quality aqua out strips the supply many people have yet to see a fine quality stone.

NAME OF GEMSTONE:

Beryl
(silicate of aluminum & beryllium)
Variety: Emerald
Color Occurrences: *emerald*
Emerald is by definition green and must have an adequate percentage of chromium to qualify as emerald and not be green beryl.

OPTICAL AND PHYSICAL PROPERTIES:

Refractive Indices: 1.577-1.583 $\pm$ 0.17

Birefringence: .005 to .009, weak
Pleochroism: Emerald -- dichroic strong
Dispersion: .014, medium
Specific Gravity: 2.67-2.84; 2.72 normal

JEWELRY PROPERTIES:

Hardness: 7 1/2-8
Cleavage: very difficult; one direction
Fracture: tough to uneven, conchoidal
Toughness: Emerald -- fair, usually flawed, brittle.
Steam Cleaning: Emerald -- not recommended

IMPORTANT SIZE: Emerald -- over 1 carat; exceedingly rare over 40 carats.
CURRENT COMMERCIALLY IMPORTANT LOCATIONS: Emerald -- Colombia; Zambia; Brazil.
COMMENTS: Emerald -- fine quality emerald can rival diamond in price per-carat. Virtually all emeralds have visible inclusions. The beauty in emerald comes primarily from its color.

NAME OF GEMSTONE:
Beryl
(silicate of aluminum & beryllium)
Variety: Morganite
Color Occurrences: *morganite*
Morganite occurs in peach, pink and
colors in between.

OPTICAL AND PHYSICAL PROPERTIES:
Refractive Indices: 1.577-1.583 ± 0.17
Birefringence: .005 to .009, weak

Pleochroism: Morganite -- dichroic: weak
to moderate.
Dispersion: .014, medium
Specific Gravity: 2.67-2.84; 2.72 normal

JEWELRY PROPERTIES:
Hardness: 7 1/2-8
Cleavage: very difficult; one direction
Fracture: tough to uneven, conchoidal
Toughness: Morganite -- fair to good
Steam Cleaning: Morganite -- not
 recommended

IMPORTANT SIZE: Morganite -- over 5 carats, rare over 100 carats.
CURRENT COMMERCIALLY IMPORTANT LOCATIONS: Morganite -- Brazil, occasionally Madagascar.
COMMENTS: Morganite -- Morganite is one of the lesser known beryls. While small quantities of morganite have normally been the rule, the price of morganite has remained at an affordable level. It would seem this is a matter of not being well known. This is a boon to the collector.

NAME OF GEMSTONE:

Chrysoberyl
(Beryllium aluminate)
Variety: Alexandrite
Color Occurrences: *alexandrite*
color changes from daylight to
incandescent light. Various hues of
green=daylight. Various hues of
 purple/red= incandescent.

OPTICAL AND PHYSICAL PROPERTIES:

Refractive Indices: 1.746 - 1.755, ±.005
Birefringence: .009, medium

Pleochroism: trichroic, weak to strong
Dispersion: .015, medium
Specific Gravity: Alexandrite 3.71-3.75;
3.73 normal

JEWELRY PROPERTIES:

Hardness: 8 1/2
Cleavage: none of importance for jewelry
purposes
Fracture: conchoidal to uneven
Toughness: good
Steam Cleaning: slow to moderate
warm-up

IMPORTANT SIZE: Alexandrite -- over .50 carat; fine stones over 3 carats difficult to obtain.

CURRENT COMMERCIALLY IMPORTANT LOCATIONS: Alexandrite -- Sri Lanka; Brazil.

COMMENTS: Alexandrite -- alexandrite is perhaps the rarest of all the well known gems. The color change phenomenon in alexandrite is quite intriguing. Interestingly enough, most color film cannot capture the color change we see with our eyes.

NAME OF GEMSTONE:
Chrysoberyl
(Beryllium aluminate)
Variety: Cat's-eye
Color Occurrences: *cat's-eye*
light golden yellow
yellow
honey-brown
olive green
brown
greenish yellow to yellow-green
brownish green
brown to brownish yellow to
yellow-brown

OPTICAL AND PHYSICAL PROPERTIES:
Refractive Indices: 1.746 - 1.755, ±.005
Birefringence: .009, medium
Pleochroism: trichroic, weak to strong
Dispersion: .015, medium
Specific Gravity: Cat's-eye -- 3.73-3.75;
 3.73 normal

JEWELRY PROPERTIES:
Hardness: 8 1/2
Cleavage: none of importance for jewelry
purposes
Fracture: conchoidal to uneven
Toughness: good
Steam Cleaning: slow to moderate
warm-up

IMPORTANT SIZE: Cat's-eye -- 1 carat; fine stones over 5 carats exceedingly difficult to obtain.

CURRENT COMMERCIALLY IMPORTANT LOCATIONS: Cat's-eye -- Sri Lanka; Brazil.

COMMENTS: Cat's-eye -- chrysoberyl cat's-eye in the optimum can be described as being a honey color. A good "eye" is one which is unbroken, well defined, and which follows the light as you turn the stone from side to side.

NAME OF GEMSTONE:

Chrysoberyl

(Beryllium aluminate)

Variety: Common Chrysoberyl
(as distinguished from
cat's-eye or alexandrite)

Color Occurrences: *common chrysoberyl*
light golden yellow
yellow
honey-brown
olive green
brown
greenish yellow to yellow-green
brownish green
brown to brownish yellow to
yellow-brown

OPTICAL AND PHYSICAL PROPERTIES:

Refractive Indices: 1.746 - 1.755, ±.005
Birefringence: .009, medium
Pleochroism: trichroic, weak to strong
Dispersion: .015, medium
Specific Gravity: Common Chrysoberyl --
3.71-3.75; 3.73 normal

JEWELRY PROPERTIES:

Hardness: 8 1/2
Cleavage: none of importance for jewelry
purposes
Fracture: conchoidal to uneven
Toughness: good
Steam Cleaning: slow to moderate
warm-up

IMPORTANT SIZE: Common chrysoberyl -- over 2 carats; fine quality stones over 10 carats are infrequetly available

CURRENT COMMERCIALLY IMPORTANT LOCATIONS: Common chrysoberyl -- Brazil, Sri Lanka.

COMMENTS: Common chrysoberyl -- the use of the word common is a bit misleading. All varieties of chrysoberyl are rare. It is simply that alexandrite and cat's-eye are exceptionally rare and expensive. Large faceted specimens of chrysoberyl are definitely collectible.

NAME OF GEMSTONE:

Corundum
(aluminum oxide)
Variety: Blue Sapphire
Color Occurrences: *sapphire*
blue
yellow and golden
pink
most colors *except* red
(red corundum is ruby)

OPTICAL AND PHYSICAL
PROPERTIES:

Refractive Indices: 1.762-1.770 + .008
                                        - .003

Birefringence: .008, weak
Pleochroism: Blue - dichroic, strong.
Dispersion: .018, medium
Specific Gravity: 3.97-4.03; 4.00 normal

JEWELRY PROPERTIES:

Hardness: 9
Cleavage: none, two parting directions in
twinned stones
Fracture: conchoidal
Toughness: excellent, except in twinned
or fractured stones
Steam Cleaning: slow to moderate
warm-up

IMPORTANT SIZE: Blue -- over 1 carat; unusual size: over 20 carats.
CURRENT COMMERCIALLY IMPORTANT LOCATIONS: Blue -- Australia;
Burma; Thailand; Sri Lanka; Montana.
COMMENTS: Blue Sapphire -- Over the past few decades most sapphires sold in
the U.S.A. have been the overly dark material from Australia. To a degree the public is
unaware of the true beauty of the gems from other locations. Thailand and Sri Lanka
produce gems that can be both beautiful yet moderately priced. Burmese gems are
often exceptional in color but have a price to match.

NAME OF GEMSTONE:

Corundum
(aluminum oxide)
Variety: Pink Sapphire
Color Occurrences: *sapphire*
blue
yellow and golden
pink
most colors *except* red
(red corundum is ruby)

OPTICAL AND PHYSICAL PROPERTIES:

Refractive Indices: 1.762-1.770 + .008
                                    - .003

Birefringence: .008, weak
Pleochroism: Pink -- dichroic, weak to strong,
Dispersion: .018, medium
Specific Gravity: 3.97-4.03; 4.00 normal

JEWELRY PROPERTIES:

Hardness: 9
Cleavage: none, two parting directions in twinned stones
Fracture: conchoidal
Toughness: excellent, except in twinned or fractured stones
Steam cleaning: slow to moderate warm-up

IMPORTANT SIZE: Pink sapphire -- begins at 1 carat; Unusual size: over 5 carats.

CURRENT COMMERCIALLY IMPORTANT LOCATIONS: Pink -- Burma; Sri Lanka; Tanzania; Vietnam.

COMMENTS: Pink Sapphire -- For novices to the gem world pink sapphire is a pleasant surprise. While there are other pink gems, pink sapphire comes in some particularly pretty hues. Also, the hardness of sapphire is a definate plus.

NAME OF GEMSTONE:

Corundum
(aluminum oxide)
Varieties: Ruby/Star Ruby
Color Occurrences: *ruby*
Ruby is the red variety of corundum
Each of the locations listed produces
rubies of different a characteristic
color variety.

Thailand	Kenya	Tanzania
Burma	Sri Lanka	India

OPTICAL AND PHYSICAL PROPERTIES:

Refractive Indices: 1.762-1.770 + .008
                                          - .003

Birefringence: .008, weak
Pleochroism: dichroic, strong
Dispersion: .018, medium
Specific Gravity: 3.97-4.03; 4.00 normal

JEWELRY PROPERTIES:

Hardness: 9
Cleavage: none, two parting directions in
twinned stones
Fracture: conchoidal
Toughness: excellent, except for twinned
or fractured stones
Steam Cleaning: slow to moderate
warm-up

IMPORTANT SIZE: Faceted Ruby -- Over 1 carat: Fine quality stones over 3 carats are currently very difficult to obtain. Indian star ruby -- size is not particularly an issue.

CURRENT COMMERCIALLY IMPORTANT LOCATIONS: Thailand; Sri Lanka; Burma; Kenya, India.

COMMENTS: Ruby -- Burmese stones generally receive a premium simply by being Burmese. The distinctive pinkish overtones are quite noticeable once you have looked at enough Burma stones. Judging color in rubies is perhaps one of the most difficult tasks a gem dealer is ever faced with. There are so many variations from the optimum and so few stones which are good examples of the optimum that it is difficult to make easy judgment.

NAME OF GEMSTONE:

Corundum
(aluminum oxide)
Variety: Yellow, Golden Sapphire
Color Occurrences: *sapphire*
blue
yellow and golden
pink
most colors *except red*
(red corundum is ruby)

OPTICAL AND PHYSICAL PROPERTIES:

Refractive Indices: 1.762-1.770 + .008
                                      - .003

Birefringence: .008, weak
Pleochroism: Yellow and golden --
dichroic, weak to strong.
Dispersion: .018, medium
Specific Gravity: 3.97-4.03; 4.00 normal

JEWELRY PROPERTIES:

Hardness: 9
Cleavage: none, two parting directions in
twinned stones
Fracture: conchoidal
Toughness: excellent, except for twinned
or fractured stones
Steam Cleaning: slow to moderate
warm-up

IMPORTANT SIZE: Yellow and Golden sapphire -- begins at 1 carat; unusual size: over 25 carats.

CURRENT COMMERCIALLY IMPORTANT LOCATIONS: Yellow and Golden -- Australia; Thailand; Montana; Sri Lanka.

COMMENTS: Yellow and Golden sapphire -- in this part of the color spectrum sapphire duplicates other gems. However, of special note with yellow and golden sapphire is the purity and intensity carried down to the 1 carat and smaller sizes. Of course, the durability is helpful as well.

NAME OF GEMSTONE:

Diamond
(pure carbon)
Variety: colorless diamonds
Color Occurrences: *diamond*

colorless	green
brown	orange
red	mauve
yellow	black
blue	

OPTICAL AND PHYSICAL PROPERTIES:

Refractive Index: 2.417

Birefringence: none
Isotropic
Dispersion: .044, strong
Specific Gravity: 3.51-3.53; 3.52 normal

JEWELRY PROPERTIES:

Hardness: 10
Cleavage: highly perfect, four directions
Fracture: conchoidal to splintery
Toughness: fair to exceptional
Steam Cleaning: moderate warm-up

IMPORTANT SIZE: Varies with the market, generally over 1 carat.

CURRENT COMMERCIALLY IMPORTANT LOCATIONS: South Africa; Brazil; Australia, Russia.

COMMENTS: "Diamond" is the single most exciting word in all of gemstones. The remarkable optical properties of diamond give it incomparable brilliance and fire. The hardness of diamond insures its owner of its long lasting nature. The trade in diamonds is so important worldwide that it can shore up the economy of a nation.

197

NAME OF GEMSTONE:

Rhodolite Garnet
(pyrope and almandite mix:
magnesium-iron-aluminum silicate)
Variety: Rhodolite
Color Occurrences: *rhodolite*
rose-red
violet
red
deep red to near-black

OPTICAL AND PHYSICAL PROPERTIES:

Refractive Index: 1.76 ± .010

Birfringence: sometimes anomalous
Dispersion: .026
Isotropic
Specific Gravity: 3.74-3.94; 3.84 normal

JEWELRY PROPERTIES:

Hardness: 7-7 1/2
Cleavage: none, parting often distinct
Fracture: sub-conchoidal to uneven
Toughness: fair to good, often brittle

Steam Cleaning: slow to moderate
warm-up

IMPORTANT SIZE: over 4 carats; unusual size over 15 carats.
CURRENT COMMERCIALLY IMPORTANT LOCATIONS: Tanzania; Sri Lanka; India.
COMMENTS: Rhodolite Garnet -- Rhodolite garnet, which is a pyrope and almandite mix, is distinguished from other reddish colored garnets by virtue of the fact that it is usually of lighter in color. Rhodolite tends to the pink. The optimum color in rhodolite is a lightish pinkish garnet color. A nice rhodolite garnet is noted for its beautiful lively color even in larger sizes.

NAME OF GEMSTONE:

Spessartite Garnet
(manganese aluminum silicate)
Variety: Spessartite
Color Occurrences: *spessartite*
orange
orangey-red
brownish orange

OPTICAL AND PHYSICAL PROPERTIES:

Refractive Index: 1.81 ± .010

Birefringence: none
sometimes anomalous
Pleochroism: not pleochroic
Dispersion: .027
Specific Gravity: 4.15

JEWELRY PROPERTIES:

7 to 7½
Cleavage: none
Fracture: sub-conchoidal to uneven
Toughness: brittle
Steam Cleaning: slow warm-up

IMPORTANT SIZE: over 2 carats; Fine stones over 5 carats are available occasionally.

CURRENT COMMERCIALLY IMPORTANT LOCATIONS: California, Brazil, Madagascar.

COMMENTS: Spessartite -- Spessartite is a fun, collectible garnet. While spessartite is available only from time to time keep an eye out and you may be lucky enough to acquire one.

NAME OF GEMSTONE:

Grossular Garnet
(calcium-aluminum silicate)
Variety: Tsavorite
Color Occurrence: *tsavorite*
medium to dark green

OPTICAL AND PHYSICAL PROPERTIES

Refractive Indices: 1.74 ± .01
Birefringence: None; sometimes exhibits
anomalous double refraction

Pleochroism: None
Dispersion: .028, medium
Specific Gravity: 3.57-3.73; 3.61 normal

JEWELRY PROPERTIES:

Hardness: 7
Cleavage: very difficult
Fracture: sub-conchoidal to uneven
Toughness: fair to good, often brittle
Steam Cleaning: slow warm-up

IMPORTANT SIZE: over one carat; Fine quality stones over 2 carats are currently very difficult to obtain.

CURRENT COMMERCIALLY IMPORTANT LOCATIONS: Kenya, Tanzania.

COMMENTS: Tsavorite -- Tsavorite, as you can tell, is a lovely very pure green color. Tsavorite is a wonderful exception to the rule of garnets being red. Tsavorite is so lovely and so rare it is a favorite collectible of gem dealers who have personal collections.

NAME OF GEMSTONES:

Olivine
(magnesium iron silicate)
Variety: Peridot
Color Occurrences: *olivine*

green	red (if oxidized)
greenish-brown	olive green
orange	grayish red
yellowish-brown	grayish green

OPTICAL AND PHYSICAL PROPERTIES:

Refractive Indices: 1.654-1.690 ± .020

Birefringence: .036, strong
Pleochroism: weak
Dispersion: .020, medium
Specific Gravity: 3.31-3.148; 3.34 normal

JEWELRY PROPERTIES:

Hardness: 6 1/2-7
Cleavage: difficult
Fracture: conchoidal, tough
Toughness: fair to good, often brittle
Steam Cleaning: slow warm-up

IMPORTANT SIZE: over 3carats; Fine stones over 10 carats are unusual.
CURRENT COMMERCIALLY IMPORTANT LOCATIONS: Arizona; Mexico; Burma; Norway.
COMMENTS: Peridot -- Peridot in the optimum color is a nice, lively, grass green. You might discern from the mineral name, olivine, most of the material tends to be an olive color. The olive brownish green is definitely a detraction in peridot. If you like a particular peridot at first glance, chances are that you are looking at the right color.

201

NAME OF GEMSTONE:
Quartz
(silicon dioxide)
Variety: Amethyst
Color Occurrences: *amethyst*
violet to red purple

OPTICAL AND PHYSICAL
PROPERTIES:
Refractive Indices: 1.544-1.553
Birefringence: .009

Pleochroism: dichroic, medium
Dispersion: .013
Specific Gravity: 2.65-2.67; 2.66 normal

JEWELRY PROPERTIES:
Hardness: 7
Cleavage: none
Fracture: conchoidal
Toughness: good
Steam Cleaning: slow warm-up

IMPORTANT SIZE: Amethyst is readily available in all sizes.
CURRENT COMMERCIALLY IMPORTANT LOCATIONS: Brazil; Uruguay; Bolivia; Zambia; South Africa.
COMMENTS: Amethyst --The optimum amethyst is a nice deep purple with flashes of red. Some inferior grades of amethyst achieve their depth of color by addding grey or brown overtones to a light or medium purple. In larger stones some localities produce stones that are too dark.

NAME OF GEMSTONE:
Quartz
(silicon dioxide)
Variety: Ametrine
Color Occurrences: *ametrine*
violet to red purple/yellow-gold

OPTICAL AND PHYSICAL PROPERTIES:
Refractive Indices: 1.544-1.553
Birefringence: .009

Pleochroism: dichroic, medium
Dispersion: .013
Specific Gravity: 2.65-2.67; 2.66 normal

JEWELRY PROPERTIES:
Hardness: 7
Cleavage: none
Fracture: conchoidal
Toughness: good
Steam Cleaning: slow warm-up

IMPORTANT SIZE: Ametrine is available in all sizes.
CURRENT COMMERCIALLY IMPORTANT LOCATIONS: Bolivia.
COMMENTS: Ametrine -- ametrine, like amethyst, is a color variety of quartz. Ametrine is a bi-colored stone displaying the purple of amethyst and the gold of citrine. These stones occur naturally only in Bolivia.

NAME OF GEMSTONE:

Quartz
(silicon dioxide)
Variety: Citrine
Color Occurrences: *citrine*
yellow, gold, orange, red

OPTICAL AND PHYSICAL
PROPERTIES:

Refractive Indices: 1.544-1.553
Birefringence: .009

Pleochroism: dichroic, medium
Dispersion: .013
Specific Gravity: 2.65-2.67; 2.66 normal

JEWELRY PROPERTIES:

Hardness: 7
Cleavage: none
Fracture: conchoidal
Toughness: good
Steam Cleaning: slow warm-up

IMPORTANT SIZE: Citrine, like amethyst, occurs in good quantities in most sizes.
CURRENT COMMERCIALLY IMPORTANT LOCATIONS: Brazil.
COMMENTS: Citrine -- citrine is a color variety of quartz that varies from yellow through red and in between. It is a lovely yet affordable natural gem. The color in citrine is virtually always the result of heat treating.

NAME OF GEMSTONE:

Spinel
(magnesium aluminum oxide)
Variety: Red Spinel
Color Occurrences: *spinel*

red	lavender
blue	orange
pink	purple

OPTICAL AND PHYSICAL PROPERTIES:

Refractive Index: 1.718 + .044
           - .006

Birefringence: none
Isotropic
Dispersion: .020 medium
Specific Gravity: 3.57-3.90; 3.60 normal

JEWELRY PROPERTIES:

Hardness: 8
Cleavage: difficult
Fracture: conchoidal
Toughness: good
Steam Cleaning: slow to moderate
warm-up

IMPORTANT SIZE: Spinel -- over 1 carat; unusual size: over 4 carats.
CURRENT COMMERCIALLY IMPORTANT LOCATIONS: Burma; Sri Lanka; Thailand.
COMMENTS: Red Spinel -- The optimum color for red spinel is ruby red. Consequently these stones have acquired the nickname "ruby-spinel." Spinels with a true ruby look come almost exclusively from Burma.

NAME OF GEMSTONE:

Spodumene
(lithium aluminum silicate)
Variety: Kunzite
Color Occurrences: *spodumene*
lavender
green
yellow to colorless
greenish-white
grayish-white
yellowish-green
emerald-green
amethystine purple
pink

OPTICAL AND PHYSICAL PROPERTIES:

Refractive Indices: 1.660-1.676 ± .005
Birefringence: .016, medium
Pleochroism: trichroic, strong to weak
Dispersion: .017, medium
Specific Gravity: 3.15-3.21; 3.18 normal

JEWELRY PROPERTIES:

Hardness: 6-7
Cleavage: highly perfect, two directions
Fracture: uneven to splintery
Toughness: poor, frays easily
Steam Cleaning: extremely sensitive: use other cleaning method

IMPORTANT SIZE: begins at 10 carats; unusual size: over 500 carats.
CURRENT COMMERCIALLY IMPORTANT LOCATIONS: Afghanistan; Brazil; California.
COMMENTS: One of the many interesting sidelights about kunzite involves geography. This material was first observed in deposits in Southern California toward the turn of the century. Plentiful at first, the California material soon gave out. The next big deposit was found in Brazil. Again, at first the material was abundant with large crystals being found. But with similarity to the California deposit, the material from Brazil gave out with intense mining. Fortunately, there was yet another kunzite repository in Afghanistan.

NAME OF GEMSTONE:

Tourmaline
(complex boron aluminum silicate)
Varieties: Indicolite
Color Occurrences: *tourmaline*
General:
    tourmaline is known as the rainbow
    gem. It occurs in virtually every color.
Indicolite:
  blue
  blue green
  blue gray

OPTICAL AND PHYSICAL PROPERTIES:

Refractive Indices: 1.624-1.644 ± .006

Birefringence: .020, medium
Pleochroism: dichroic, strong
Dispersion: .017, medium
Specific Gravity: 3.01-3.21; 3.06 normal

JEWELRY PROPERTIES:

Hardness: 7-7 1/2
Cleavage: difficult
Fracture: sub-conchoidal to uneven
Toughness: fair
Steam Cleaning: extremely sensitive: use other method

IMPORTANT SIZE: Indicolite -- over 3 carats; fine stones over 10 carats are unusual.

CURRENT COMMERCIALLY IMPORTANT LOCATIONS: Indicolite -- Brazil; Afghanistan.

COMMENTS: Indiolite -- as you may guess from the word "indigo," indicolite covers the blue part of the tourmaline color spectrum. Any indicolite from medium quality up is in great demand.

NAME OF GEMSTONE:

Tourmaline
(complex boron aluminum silicate)
Variety: Rose tourmaline
Color Occurrences: *tourmaline*
Rose tourmaline:
> Intense pink with slight violet
> overtones to brownish rose pink.
> Intense pink with slight
> violet overtones to pale pink.

OPTICAL AND PHYSICAL PROPERTIES:

Refractive Indices: 1.624-1.644 ± .006

Birefringence: .020, medium
Pleochroism: dichroic, strong
Dispersion: .017, medium
Specific Gravity: 3.01-3.21; 3.06 normal

JEWELRY PROPERTIES:

Hardness: 7-7 1/2
Cleavage: difficult
Fracture: sub-conchoidal to uneven
Toughness: fair
Steam Cleaning: extremely sensitive:
use other method

IMPORTANT SIZE: Rose Tourmaline -- over 3 carats; fine stones over 20 carats are unusual.

CURRENT COMMERCIAL IMPORTANT LOCATIONS: Brazil; Afghanistan; Mozambique.

COMMENTS: Rose Tourmaline -- Rose tourmaline is somewhat a bridge of the gap between rubellite and pure pink tourmaline. Rose tourmaline tends in the best stones to be an extremely intense pink with slight violet overtones at the optimum.

NAME OF GEMSTONE:

Tourmaline
(complex boron aluminum silicate)
Variety: Rubellite
Color Occurrences: *tourmaline*
Rubellite: Hot pink to red
General:
   Tourmaline is known as the
   rainbow gem. It occurs in
   virtually every color.

OPTICAL AND PHYSICAL PROPERTIES:

Refractive Indices: 1.624-1.644 ± .006

Birefringence: .020, medium
Pleochroism: dichroic,, strong
Dispersion: .017, medium
Specific Gravity: 3.01-3.21; 3.06 normal

JEWELRY PROPERTIES:

Hardness: 7-7 1/2
Cleavage: difficult
Fracture: sub-conchoidal to uneven
Toughness: fair
Steam Cleaning: extremely sensitive:
use other method

IMPORTANT SIZE: Rubellite -- over 3 carats; fine stones over 10 carats are unusual.

CURRENT COMMERCIALLY IMPORTANT LOCATIONS: Brazil; Afghanistan; Mozambique.

COMMENTS: Rubellite Tourmaline -- Rubellite tourmaline is that variety of tourmaline which has a nice red color. The primary overtones in a nice rubellite are either orange or pink. Also note that rubellite and the hot-pink tourmalines associated with it almost always have some inclusions and are accepted with them. The degree to which a rubellite is included will affect its price.

209

NAME OF GEMSTONE:

Topaz
(fluosilicate of aluminum)
Varieties: Imperial
         Pink
Color Occurrences: *topaz*

orange	blue	yellow
pink	brown	golden
red	lavender	

OPTICAL AND PHYSICAL PROPERTIES:

Refractive Indices: 1.619-1.627 ± .010

Birefringence: .008, weak
Pleochroism: dichroic, strong to weak
Dispersion: .014, medium
Specific Gravity: 3.49-3.57; 3.53 normal

JEWELRY PROPERTIES:

Hardness: 8
Cleavage: highly perfect, one direction
Fracture: conchoidal
Toughness: poor
Steam Cleaning: sensitive: use other cleaning method

IMPORTANT SIZE: Imperial -- over 3 carats; fine stones over 10 carats are unusual. Pink -- begins at 3 carats; unusual size: over 10 carats.

CURRENT COMMERCIALLY IMPORTANT LOCATIONS: Pakistan; Brazil.

COMMENTS: Imperial Topaz -- Imperial topaz is the variety of topaz which comes solely from Ouro Preto, Brazil. This is a very unusual type of topaz in its color. The choice for optimum in Imperial topaz is an orangey-red color.

COMMENTS: Pink Topaz -- Pink topaz comes primarily from Brazil and Pakistan.

In addition to Imperial topaz and pink topaz there are a couple of rare items available once in a while in a truly red topaz or in a lavender topaz. Besides the red stones and lavender stones occasionally there will occur a bi-colored topaz. These bi-colored stones are usually part orange and part red or lavender.

NAME OF GEMSTONE:

Zoisite
(calcium aluminum silicate)
Variety: Tanzanite
Color Occurrences: *Zoisite*
colorless
pink
blue
violet
orange
peach-blossom to rose red
grayish-white
gray
yellowish brown
greenish gray
apple green

OPTICAL AND PHYSICAL PROPERTIES:

Refractive Indices; 1.691-1.704 ± .003
Birefringence: .013, weak
Pleochroism: trichroic, strong
Dispersion: .021
Specific Gravity: 3.20-3.40; 3.30 normal

JEWELRY PROPERTIES:

Hardness: 6 to 7
Cleavage: perfect; one direction
Fracture: uneven to sub-conchoidal
Toughness: fair to good, brittle
Steam Cleaning: extremely sensitive:
use other cleaning method

IMPORTANT SIZE: begins over 2 carats; unusual size: over 10 carats.
CURRENT COMMERCIALLY IMPORTANT LOCATIONS: Tanzania.
COMMENTS: Tanzanite was destined to be a popular gem due to its fabulous color.
Virtually all people of the world love tanzanite. Since it is a one location gem there is
no telling how long supplies will last.

NAME OF GEMSTONE:

Amber
(fossilized tree resin)
Variety: amber
Color Occurrences: *amber*
light yellow to golden yellow, orange
through red, brown

OPTICAL AND PHYSICAL PROPERTIES:

Refractive Indices: 1.540 + .005
                              - .001

Birefringence: none
Pleochroism: none
Specific Gravity: 1.00 - 1.10; 1.08 normal

JEWELRY PROPERTIES:

Hardness: 2 - 2 ½
Cleavage: none
Fracture: conchoidal
Toughness: poor
Steam Cleaning: use other method

IMPORTANT SIZE: Amber -- over 10 carats; unusual size over 50 carats.

CURRENT COMMERCIALLY IMPORTANT LOCATIONS: Dominican Republic, Baltic Coast.

COMMENTS: Amber is best known from the Baltic region. It is of organic orgin and is fossilized. This fact combined with its unusual inclusions of whole insects and other once-living matter makes amber a spark for the imagination.

NAME OF GEMSTONE:

Apatite
(Calcium fluo-phosphate)
Variety: Apatite
Color Occurrences: *apatite*
colorless, brown, blue, green, yellow,
purple pink, lavender

OPTICAL AND PHYSICAL PROPERTIES:

Refractive Indices: 1.64 + .012
                              - .006

Birefringence: .002 - .008
Pleochroism: weak to strong
Dispersion: .013, medium
Specific Gravity: 3.13 - 3.23

JEWELRY PROPERTIES:

Hardness: 5
Cleavage: imperfect
Fracture: chonchoidal
Toughness: fair
Steam Cleaning: use other method

IMPORTANT SIZE: "Neon" blue and green, begins at one carat; unusual over 3 carats. Colorless, brown and yellow, begins at 3 carats; unusual over 5 carats. Purple, pink and lavender begins at 2 carats; unusual over 4 carats.

CURRENT COMMERCIALLY IMPORTANT LOCATIONS: Madagascar. Other locations not commercially significant.

COMMENTS: Apatite has usually been only for the collector of rare and esoteric gems. The fairly recent find of "Neon" colors from Madagascar has created a demand for apatite in jewelry as well.

NAME OF GEMSTONE:

Iolite
(Magnesium Aluminum Silicate)
Variety: Iolite (also known as Cordierite)
Color Occurrences: *iolite*
blue, violet and violetish blue. Ranging
from pale to dark. Occasionally gray,
green or yellow

OPTICAL AND PHYSICAL PROPERTIES:

Refractive Indices: 1.542 - 1.551 + .045
                                        - .011

Birefringence: .009 medium
Pleochroism: strong
Dispersion: .017
Specific Gravity: 2.56 - 2.66
                             2.61 normal

JEWELRY PROPERTIES:

Hardness: 7 - 7 ½
Cleavage: Distinct, one direction
Fracture: uneven to conchoidal
Toughness: fair
Steam Cleaning: use other method

IMPORTANT SIZE: Begins at 2 carats; unusual over 8 carats.
CURRENT COMMERCIALLY IMPORTANT LOCATIONS: India
COMMENTS: Iolite has remained unexposed and unknown to the public until recently. Exposure has found Iolite to be well received by the public.

NAME OF GEMSTONE:

Lapis lazuli
(a rock composed mostly of lazurite,
pyrite and calcate)
Variety: Lapis lazuli
Color Occurrences:
blue--medium to dark ranging from
greenish to violetish. Can show calcite
and/or pyrite inclusions.

OPTICAL AND PHYSICAL PROPERTIES:

Refractive Index: 1.50

Birefringence: none
Pleochroism: none
Dispersion: none
Specific Gravity: 2.75 ± .25

JEWELRY PROPERTIES:

Hardness: 5-6
Cleavage: none
Fracture: uneven
Toughness: fair
Steam Cleaning: use other method

IMPORTANT SIZE: Lapis lazuli comes in large pieces. Size is not important in pieces suitable for jewelry.
CURRENT COMMERCIALLY IMPORTANT LOCATIONS: Afghanistan (best material), Chile (inferior material).
COMMENTS: Lapis is one of the most ancient of gems. Worked pieces of lapis have been found in ancient tombs including those of ancient Egypt.

NAME OF GEMSTONE:

Malachite
(Copper Carbonate)
Variety: Malachite
Color Occurrences: *malachite*
green, usualy banded with several colors
of green.

Can range from yellow green--to green--
to bluishgreen.

OPTICAL AND PHYSICAL PROPERTIES:

Refractive Indices: 1.65-1.90

Birefringence: .25 strong
Pleochroism: none
Dispersion: none
Specific Gravity: 3.95 - normal

JEWELRY PROPERTIES:

Hardness: 3½ to 4.0
Cleavage: Perfect two directions
Fracture: uneven
Toughness: poor
Steam Cleaning: use other method

IMPORTANT SIZE: Occurs in large pieces. Size is not an issue in pieces suitable for jewelry.

CURRENT COMMERCIALLY IMPORTANT LOCATIONS: Zaire

COMMENTS: Malachite gives us an affordable vivid green gem. Virtually any jewelry size is inexpensive; proof that in gemstones beauty can be for everybody.

NAME OF GEMSTONE:

Opal
(Hydrous Silcon Dioxide)
Varieties: Common
       Cherry and Fire
       Precious
Color Occurrences: *common opal*
translucent to opaque white, yellow
orange, red, blue, lavender
Cherry and fire: range of orange to red
orange.
Precious - any of above body colors plus
play of color

OPTICAL AND PHYSICAL PROPERTIES:

Refractive Indices: 1.45 + .020
                       - .080
Birefringence: none
Pleochroism: none
Dispersion: none
Specific Gravity: 1.90 - 2.30

JEWELRY PROPERTIES:

Hardness: 5-6½
Cleavage: none
Fracture: conchoidal to uneven
Toughness: poor to fair
Steam Cleaning: use other method

IMPORTANT SIZE: Cherry and fire opal begins at 1 carat; unusual over 5 carats. Precious opal begins at 2 carats; unusual over 40 carats in fine quality. Black Lightening Ridge begins at 1 carat; unusual over 10 carats.

CURRENT COMMERCIALLY IMPORTANT LOCATIONS: Mexico, Australia, Brazil.

COMMENTS: Opal occurs in such different looking gems from its various localities that it is a fascinating gem. For this reason people are known to collect opals to the exclusion of other gems. Whole books have been devoted to opal.

NAME OF GEMSTONE:

Scapolite
(Aluminum Silcate)
Variety: Scapolite
Color Occurrences: *scapolite*
yellow, gold, orange, purple, green, blue,
pink

Birefringence: .004 to .037
Dispersion: .017
Pleochroism: varies with color variety,
generally moderate to strong
Specific Gravity: 2.62 - 2.74
2.68 normal

OPTICAL AND PHYSICAL PROPERTIES:

Refractive Indices: 1.550 - 1.564 + .015
- .014

JEWELRY PROPERTIES:

Hardness: 6 - 6 ½
Cleavage: perfect - 2 directions
Fracture: conchoidal
Toughness: fair
Steam Cleaning: use other method

IMPORTANT SIZE: Yellow and gold, over 5 carats; unusual size over 25 carats. Purple, over 1 carat, unusual over 3 carats.

CURRENT COMMERCIALLY IMPORTANT LOCATIONS: Tanzania, Kenya, Brazil, Burma.

COMMENTS: East Africa is known for occasional production of large, clean scapolite crystals that can cut beautiful golden to orange gems from 5 to 50 carats. Also from the region is material in an intense purple that produces gems from sub-carat size up to as much as 5 carats.

NAME OF GEMSTONE:

Plagioclase feldspar
(Aluminum Silicate)
Variety: Sunstone
Color Occurrences: *sunstone*
pale yellow, pink, red, green with pink,
pale yellow with green or pink or red, can
include reflective inclusions of hematite
called "schiller".

Birefringence: .007 to .010
Pleochroism: weak
Dispersion: .012
Specific Gravity: 2.65 - 2.67

JEWELRY PROPERTIES:

Hardness: 6 - 6 ½
Cleavage: perfect
Fracture: uneven
Toughness: poor
Steam Cleaning: use other method

OPTICAL AND PHYSICAL PROPERTIES:

Refractive Indices: 1.537 - 1.547 + .004
- .006

IMPORTANT SIZE: begins at 2 carats; unusual in good colors over 5 carats.

CURRENT COMMERCIALLY IMPORTANT LOCATIONS: Oregon, USA

COMMENTS: Sunstone is the Oregon state gemstone. Essentially this is a one-location gemstone in the facetable material. The cabochon material has a similar looking occurrence in India.

NAME OF GEMSTONE:

Zircon
(Zirconium Silicate)
Variety: Zircon
Color Occurrences:
colorless, pale to medium blue, green,
brown, red, violet, orange

OPTICAL AND PHYSICAL PROPERTIES:

Refractive Indices:
low zircon 1.810 - 1.815 ± .030
medium zircon 1.875 - 1.905 ± .030
high zircon 1.925 - 1.984 ± .040
Birefringence:
low zircon .002 to .005
medium zircon .006 to .050
high zircon .059

Pleochroism - weak to strong depending
on color variety
Dispersion: .038
Specific Gravity:
low zircon 3.93 - 4.07, 4.00 normal
medium zircon 4.07 - 4.57, 4.32 normal
high zircon 4.67 - 4.73, 4.70 normal

JEWELRY PROPERTIES:

Hardness: low zircon 6 ½
medium zircon 7 ½
high zircon 7 ½
Toughness: generally fair to good
Cleavage: none
Fracture: conchoidal
Steam Cleaning: better use other method

IMPORTANT SIZE: Blue, over 2 carats, unusual over 10 carats; orange, over 2 carats, unusual over 5 carats; red, over 2 carats, unusual over 5 carats.

COMMENTS: The wonderful optical properties of zircon have made it a favorite collector's stone for many years. Recent discoveries of unusual colors in Tanzania have added interest for the serious gem collector. Zircon is rare enough that it always seems hard to find when you are looking for it.

PROPERTIES OF GEMSTONES LISTED ALPHABETICALLY BY GEMSTONE

Name	Refractive Index	Birefrin-gence	Specific Gravity	Hard-ness
Actinolite	1.614-1.641 + .014	.025	3.00-3.20 3.10 Normal	5-6
Albite Feldspar	1.525-1.536	.011	2.605	6-6½
Alexandrite Chrysoberyl	1.746-1.755 ± .005	.009	3.71-3.75 3.73 Normal	8½
Almandite Garnet	1.79 ± .030	—	3.93-4.17 4.05 Normal	7½
Amber	1.54	—	1.06-1.10 1.08 Normal	2-2½
Amblygonite	1.612-1.636	.024	3.02	6
Amethyst Quartz	1.544-1.553	.009	2.65-2.67 2.66 Normal	7
Andalusite	1.634-1.643 ± .005	.008 to .013	3.13-3.21 3.17 Normal	7-7½
Apatite	1.642-1.646 + .005 − .014	.002 to .006	3.16-3.20 3.18 Normal	5
Apophylite	1,535-1.537	.002	2.30-2.50 2.40 Normal	4½-5
Aquamarine Beryl	1.577-1.583 ± .017	.005 to .009	2.67-2.84 2.72 Normal	7½-8
Aragonite	1.530-1.685	.155	2.94	3½-4
Augelite	1.574-1.588	.014	2.70	5
Axinite	1.678-1.688 ± .005	.010	3.27-3.31 3.29 Normal	6½-7
Azurite	1.73-1.84 ± .010	.11	3.30-3.87 3.80 Normal	3½-4
Barite	1.636-1.648	.012	4.50	3-3½
Benitoite	1.757-1.804	.047	3.61-3.67 3.64 Normal	6-6½
Beryl	1.577-1.583 ± .017	.005 to .009	2.67-2.84 2.72 Normal	7½-8
Beryllonite	1.552-1.562	.010	2.83-2.87 2.85 Normal	5½-6
Brazilianite	1.602-1.621 ± .003	.019	2.91-2.97 2.94 Normal	5½
Calcite	1.486-1.658	.172	2.69-2.71 2.70 Normal	3
Cassiterite	1.997-2.098 + .008 − .006	.096	6.87-7.03 6.95 Normal	6-7

Name	Refractive Index	Birefrin-gence	Specific Gravity	Hard-ness
Cat's-eye Chrysoberyl	1.746-1.755 ± .005	.009	3.71-3.75 3.73 Normal	8½
Chrysoberyl	1.746-1.755 ± .005	.009	3.71-3.75 3.73 Normal	8½
Clinozoisite	1.724-1.734 − .090	.010	3.21-3.38	6½
Copal	1.54	—	1.06	2
Cubic Zirconia	2.15	—	5.60-5.95	8-8½
Danburite	1.630-1.636 ± .003	.006	2.99-3.01 3.00 Normal	7
Datolite	1.626-1.670	.044	2.90-3.00 2.95 Normal	5-5½
Demantoid Garnet	1.875 ± .020	—	3.81-3.87 3.84 Normal	6½-7
Diamond	2.417	—	3.51-3.53 3.52 Normal	10
Diopside	1.675-1.701 + .029 − .010	.026	3.26-3.32 3.29 Normal	5-6
Dioptase	1.655-1.708 ± .012	.053	3.25-3.35 3.30 Normal	5
Dumortierite	1.678-1.689	.011	3.20-3.40 3.30 Normal	7
Ekanite	1.597	—	3.28	6-6½
Emerald Beryl	1.577-1.583 ± .017	.005 to .009	2.67-2.84 2.72 Normal	7½-8
Enstatite	1.658-1.668 ± .005	.010	3.23-3.27 3.25 Normal	5½
Epidote	1.729-1.768 + .012 − .035	.019 to .045	3.32-3.48 3.40 Normal	6-7
Euclase	1.654-1.673 ± .004	.019	3.09-3.11 3.10 Normal	7½
Fluorite	1.434	—	3.17-3.19 3.18 Normal	4
G.G.G. (Gadolinium Gallium Garnet)	2.03	—	7.05	6½
Gahnite	1.80	—	4.0-4.6	7½
Gahnospinel	1.76	—	3.61-4.41 4.01 Normal	7½
Grossular Garnet	1.74 ± .01	—	3.57-3.73 3.61 Normal	7
Hambergite	1.555-1.626 ± .002	.071	2.35	7½
Hemimorphite	1.614-1.636	.022	3.40-3.50 3.45 Normal	4½-5
Hessonite Garnet	1.74 ± .01	—	3.57-3.73 3.61 Normal	7
Hiddenite Spodumene	1.660-1.676 ± .005	.016	3.15-3.21 3.18 Normal	6-7

Name	Refractive Index	Birefringence	Specific Gravity	Hardness
Idocrase	1.713-1.718 ± .013	.005	3.30-3.50 3.40 Normal	6½
Iolite	1.542-1.551 + .045 − .011	.009	2.56-2.66 2.61 Normal	7-7½
Jadeite Jade	1.66	—	3.30-3.38 3.34 Normal	6½-7
Kornerupine	1.667-1.680 ± .003	.013	3.25-3.35 3.30 Normal	6½
Kunzite Spodumene	1.660-1.676 ± .005	.016	3.15-3.21 3.18 Normal	6-7
Kyanite	1.716-1.731 ± .004	.015	3.56-3.68 3.62 Normal	4-7
Labradorite Feldspar	1.559-1.568	.009	2.65-2.75 2.70 Normal	6
Lazulite	1.612-1.643	.031	3.04-3.14 3.09 Normal	5-6
Leucite	1.508 + .001 − .004	—	2.50	5½-6
Linobate	2.21-2.30	.09	4.64	5½
Moldavite	1.50 ± .01	—	2.36-2.44 2.40 Normal	5½
Morganite Beryl	1.577-1.583 ± .017	.005 to .009	2.67-2.84 2.72 Normal	7½-8
Natrolite	1.480-1.493	.013	2.20-2.26 2.23 Normal	5-5½
Nephrite Jade	1.60	—	2.90-3.00 2.95 Normal	6-6½
Obsidian	1.50 ± .020	—	2.35-2.55 2.45 Normal	5-5½
Oligoclase Feldspar	1.539-1.547	.008	2.64	6-6½
Opal	1.45 + .020 − .080	—	1.90-2.22 2.15 Normal	5-6½
Orthoclase Feldspar	1.518-1.526	.008	2.55-2.57 2.56 Normal	6-6½
Painite	1.787-1.816	.029	4.01	8
Peridot	1.654-1.690 ± .020	.036	3.31-3.48 3.34 Normal	6½-7
Petalite	1.502-1.518	.016	2.40	6
Phenakite	1.654-1.670 + .026 − .004	.016	2.94-2.96 2.95 Normal	7½-8
Phosphophylite	1.595-1.616	.021	3.08	3-4
Pollucite	1.520 ± .005	—	2.90-2.94 2.92 Normal	6½
Prosopite	1.501-1.510 ± .003	.009	2.89	4½
Pyrope Garnet	1.746 + .010 − .026	—	3.62-3.87 3.78 Normal	7-7½
Quartz	1.544-1.553	.009	2.65-2.67 2.66 Normal	7

Name	Refractive Index		Birefringence	Specific Gravity	Hardness
Rhodizite	1.69		—	3.40	8
Rhodochrosite	1.597-1.817	± .003	.220	3.70	3½-4½
Rhodolite Garnet	1.760	± .010	—	3.74-3.94 3.84 Normal	7-7½
Ruby Corundum	1.762-1.770	+ .008 − .003	.008	3.97-4.03 4.00 Normal	9
Rutile	2.616-2.903		.287	4.24-4.28 4.26 Normal	6-6½
Sapphire Corundum	1.762-1.770	+ .008 − .003	.008	3.97-4.03 4.00 Normal	9
Scapolite	1.550-1.572	± .002	.015 to .022	2.62-2.74 2.68 Normal	6½
Scheelite	1.918-1.934		.016	6.12	5
Sillimanite	1.659-1.680		.015 to .021	3.22-3.26 3.24 Normal	6-7
Sinhalite	1.668-1.707	± .003	.039	3.46-3.50 3.48 Normal	6-7
Sodalite	1.483	± .003	—	2.19-2.29 2.24 Normal	5-6
Spessartite Garnet	1.81	± .010	—	4.12-4.18 4.15 Normal	7-7½
Sphalerite	2.37		—	4.03-4.07 4.05 Normal	3½-4
Sphene	1.900-2.034	± .020	.10 to .135	3.50-3.54 3.52 Normal	5-5½
Spinel	1.718	+ .044 − .006	—	3.57-3.90 3.60 Normal	8
Spodumene	1.660-1.676	± .005	.016	3.15-3.21 3.18 Normal	6-7
Staurolite	1.736-1.746		.010	3.65-3.77 3.71 Normal	7-7½
Stibiotantalite	2.37-2.45		.08	7.20-7.80 7.50 Normal	5
Strontium Titanate	2.409		—	5.11-5.15 5.13 Normal	5-6
Sugilite	1.61		—	2.74	6-6½
Taaffeite	1.719-1.723	− .002	.004 to .005	3.61	8
Tanzanite Zoisite	1.691-1.704	± .003	.013	3.20-3.40 3.30 Normal	6-7
Topaz	1.619-1.627	± .010	.008	3.49-3.57 3.53 Normal	8
Tourmaline	1.624-1.644	± .006	.020	3.01-3.21 3.06 Normal	7-7½
Tsavorite Garnet	1.74	± .01	—	3.57-3.73 3.61 Normal	7
Turquoise	1.61		—	2.31-2.84 2.76 Normal	5-6
Willemite	1.691-1.719		.028	3.90-4.10 4.00 Normal	5½
Wulfenite	2.28-2.40		.12	6.5-7.0	2¾-3

Name	Refractive Index	Birefrin-gence	Specific Gravity	Hard ness
Y.A.G. (Yttrium Aluminum Garnet)	1.833	—	4.55	8¼
Zincite	2.013-2.029	.016	5.70	4-4½
Zircon (high)	1.925-1.984 ± .040	.059	4.67-4.73 4.70 Normal	7½
Zircon (medium)	1.875-1.905 ± .030	.006 to .050	4.07-4.57 4.32 Normal	7½
Zircon (low)	1.810-1.815 ± .030	.002 to .005	3.93-4.07 4.00 Normal	6½
Zoisite	1.691-1.704 ± .003	.013	3.20-3.40 3.30 Normal	6-7

PROPERTIES OF GEMSTONES LISTED NUMERICALLY BY REFRACTIVE INDEX

Name	Refractive Index		Birefrin-gence	Specific Gravity	Hard-ness
Fluorite	1.434		—	3.17-3.19 3.18 Normal	4
Opal	1.45	+ .020 − .080	—	1.90-2.22 2.15 Normal	5-6½
Natrolite	1.480-1.493		.013	2.20-2.26 2.23 Normal	5-5½
Sodalite	1.483	± .003	—	2.19-2.29 2.24 Normal	5-6
Calcite	1.486-1.658		.172	2.69-2.71 2.70 Normal	3
Moldavite	1.50	± .01	—	2.36-2.44 2.40 Normal	5½
Obsidian	1.50	± .020	—	2.35-2.55 2.45 Normal	5-5½
Prosopite	1.501-1.510	± .003	.009	2.89	4½
Petalite	1.502-1.518		.016	2.40	6
Leucite	1.508	+ .001 − .004	—	2.50	5½-6
Orthoclase Feldspar	1.518-1.526		.008	2.55-2.57 2.56 Normal	6-6½
Pollucite	1.520	± .005	—	2.90-2.94 2.92 Normal	6½
Albite Feldspar	1.525-1.536		.011	2.605	6-6½
Aragonite	1.530-1.685		.155	2.94	3½-4
Apophylite	1.535-1.537		.002	2.30-2.50 2.40 Normal	4½-5
Oligoclase Feldspar	1.539-1.547		.008	2.64	6-6½
Amber	1.54		—	1.06-1.10 1.08 Normal	2-2½
Copal	1.54		—	1.06	2
Iolite	1.542-1.551	+ .045 − .011	.009	2.56-2.66 2.61 Normal	7-7½
Quartz	1.544-1.553		.009	2.65-2.67 2.66 Normal	7
Amethyst Quartz	1.544-1.553		.009	2.65-2.67 2.66 Normal	7
Scapolite	1.550-1.572	± .002	.015 to .022	2.62-2.74 2.68 Normal	6½
Beryllonite	1.552-1.562		.010	2.83-2.87 2.85 Normal	5½-6

Name	Refractive Index	Birefringence	Specific Gravity	Hardness
Hambergite	1.555-1.626 ± .002	.071	2.35	7½
Labradorite Feldspar	1.559-1.568	.009	2.65-2.75 2.70 Normal	6
Augelite	1.574-1.588	.014	2.70	5
Aquamarine Beryl	1.577-1.583 ± .017	.005 to .009	2.67-2.84 2.72 Normal	7½-8
Emerald Beryl	1.577-1.583 ± .017	.005 to .009	2.67-2.84 2.72 Normal	7½-8
Morganite Beryl	1.577-1.583 ± .017	.005 to .009	2.67-2.84 2.72 Normal	7½-8
Beryl	1.577-1.583 ± .017	.005 to .009	2.67-2.84 2.72 Normal	7½-8
Phosphophylite	1.595-1.616	.021	3.08	3-4
Ekanite	1.597	—	3.28	6-6½
Rhodochrosite	1.597-1.817 ± .003	.220	3.70	3½-4½
Nephrite Jade	1.60	—	2.90-3.00 2.95 Normal	6-6½
Brazilianite	1.602-1.621 ± .003	.019	2.91-2.97 2.94 Normal	5½
Sugilite	1.61	—	2.74	6-6½
Turqoise	1.61	—	2.31-2.84 2.76 Normal	5-6
Amblygonite	1.612-1.636	.024	3.02	6
Lazulite	1.612-1.643	.031	3.04-3.14 3.09 Normal	5-6
Hemimorphite	1.614-1.636	.022	3.40-3.50 3.45 Normal	4½-5
Actinolite	1.614-1.641 + .014	.025	3.00-3.20 3.10 Normal	5-6
Topaz	1.619-1.627 ± .010	.008	3.49-3.57 3.53 Normal	8
Datolite	1.626-1.670	.044	2.90-3.00 2.95 Normal	5-5½
Tourmaline	1.624-1.644 ± .006	.020	3.01-3.21 3.06 Normal	7-7½
Danburite	1.630-1.636 ± .003	.006	2.99-3.01 3.00 Normal	7
Andalusite	1.634-1.643 ± .005	.008 to .013	3.13-3.21 3.17 Normal	7-7½
Barite	1.636-1.648	.012	4.50	3-3½
Apatite	1.642-1.646 + .005 − .014	.002 to .006	3.16-3.20 3.18 Normal	5
Phenakite	1.654-1.670 + .026 − .004	.016	2.94-2.96 2.95 Normal	7½-8
Euclase	1.654-1.673 ± .004	.019	3.09-3.11 3.10 Normal	7½

Name	Refractive Index		Birefringence	Specific Gravity	Hardness
Peridot	1.654-1.690	±.020	.036	3.31-3.48 3.34 Normal	6½-7
Dioptase	1.655-1.708	±.012	.053	3.25-3.35 3.30 Normal	5
Enstatite	1.658-1.668	±.005	.010	3.23-3.27 3.25 Normal	5½
Sillimanite	1.659-1.680		.015 to .021	3.22-3.26 3.24 Normal	6-7
Jadeite Jade	1.66		—	3.30-3.38 3.34 Normal	6½-7
Hiddenite Spodumene	1.660-1.676	±.005	.016	3.15-3.21 3.18 Normal	6-7
Kunzite Spodumene	1.660-1.676	±.005	.016	3.15-3.21 3.18 Normal	6-7
Spodumene	1.660-1.676	±.005	.016	3.15-3.21 3.18 Normal	6-7
Kornerupine	1.667-1.680	±.003	.013	3.25-3.35 3.30 Normal	6½
Sinhalite	1.668-1.707	±.003	.039	3.46-3.50 3.48 Normal	6-7
Diopside	1.675-1.701	+.029 -.010	.026	3.26-3.32 3.29 Normal	5-6
Axinite	1.678-1.688	±.005	.010	3.27-3.31 3.29 Normal	6½-7
Dumortierite	1.678-1.689		.011	3.20-3.40 3.30 Normal	7
Rhodizite	1.69		—	3.40	8
Tanzanite Zoisite	1.691-1.704	±.003	.013	3.20-3.40 3.30 Normal	6-7
Willemite	1.691-1.719		.028	3.90-4.10 4.00 Normal	5½
Idocrase	1.713-1.718	±.013	.005	3.30-3.50 3.40 Normal	6½
Kyanite	1.716-1.731	±.004	.015	3.56-3.68 3.62 Normal	4-7
Spinel	1.718	+.044 -.006	—	3.57-3.90 3.60 Normal	8
Taaffeite	1.719-1.723	-.002	.004 to .005	3.61	8
Clinozoisite	1.724-1.734	-.090	.010	3.21-3.38	6½
Epidote	1.729-1.768	+.012 -.035	.019 to .045	3.32-3.48 3.40 Normal	6-7
Azurite	1.73-1.84	±.010	.11	3.30-3.87 3.80 Normal	3½-4
Staurolite	1.736-1.746		.010	3.65-3.77 3.71 Normal	7-7½
Grossular Garnet	1.74	±.01	—	3.57-3.73 3.61 Normal	7
Hessonite Garnet	1.74	±.01	—	3.57-3.73 3.61 Normal	7
Tsavorite Garnet	1.74	±.01	—	3.57-3.73 3.61 Normal	7

224

Name	Refractive Index		Birefringence	Specific Gravity	Hardness
Alexandrite Chrysoberyl	1.746-1.755	± .005	.009	3.71-3.75 3.73 Normal	8½
Cat's-eye Chrysoberyl	1.746-1.755	± .005	.009	3.71-3.75 3.73 Normal	8½
Chrysoberyl	1.746-1.755	± .005	.009	3.71-3.75 3.73 Normal	8½
Pyrope Garnet	1.746	+ .010 − .026	—	3.62-3.87 3.78 Normal	7-7½
Benitoite	1.757-1.804		.047	3.61-3.67 3.64 Normal	6-6½
Gahnospinel	1.76		—	3.61-4.41 4.01 Normal	7½
Rhodolite Garnet	1.760	± .010	—	3.74-3.94 3.84 Normal	7-7½
Ruby Corundum	1.762-1.770	+ .008 − .003	.008	3.97-4.03 4.00 Normal	9
Sapphire Corundum	1.762-1.770	+ .008 − .003	.008	3.97-4.03 4.00 Normal	9
Painite	1.787-1.816		.029	4.01	8
Almandite Garnet	1.79	± .030	—	3.93-4.17 4.05 Normal	7½
Gahnite	1.80		—	4.0-4.6	7½
Spessartite Garnet	1.81	± .010	—	4.12-4.18 4.15 Normal	7-7½
Zircon (low)	1.810-1.815	± .030	.002 to .005	3.93-4.07 4.00 Normal	6½
Y.A.G. (Yttrium Aluminum Garnet)	1.833		—	4.55	8¼
Demantoid Garnet	1.875	± .020	—	3.81-3.87 3.84 Normal	6½-7
Zircon (medium)	1.875-1.905	± .030	.006 to .050	4.07-4.57 4.32 Normal	7½
Sphene	1.900-2.034	± .020	.10 to .135	3.50-3.54 3.52 Normal	5-5½
Scheelite	1.918-1.934		.016	6.12	5
Zircon (high)	1.925-1.984	± .040	.059	4.67-4.73 4.70 Normal	7½
Cassiterite	1.997-2.098	+ .008 − .006	.096	6.87-7.03 6.95 Normal	6-7
Zincite	2.013-2.029		.016	5.70	4-4½
G.G.G. (Gadolinium Gallium Garnet)	2.03		—	7.05	6½
Cubic Zirconia	2.15		—	5.60-5.95	8-8½
Linobate	2.21-2.30		.09	4.64	5½

Name	Refractive Index	Birefrin-gence	Specific Gravity	Hard-ness
Wulfenite	2.28-2.40	.12	6.5-7.0	2¾-3
Sphalerite	2.37	—	4.03-4.07 4.05 Normal	3½-4
Stibiotantalite	2.37-2.45	.08	7.20-7.80 7.50 Normal	5
Strontium Titanate	2.409	—	5.11-5.15 5.13 Normal	5-6
Diamond	2.417	—	3.51-3.53 3.52 Normal	10
Rutile	2.616-2.903	.287	4.24-4.28 4.26 Normal	6-6½

PROPERTIES OF GEMSTONES LISTED NUMERICALLY BY SPECIFIC GRAVITY

Name	Refractive Index		Birefrin-gence	Specific Gravity	Hard-ness
Copal	1.54		—	1.06	2
Amber	1.54		—	1.06-1.10 1.08 Normal	2-2½
Opal	1.45	+ .020 − .080	—	1.90-2.22 2.15 Normal	5-6½
Natrolite	1.480-1.493		.013	2.20-2.26 2.23 Normal	5-5½
Sodalite	1.483	± .003	—	2.19-2.29 2.24 Normal	5-6
Hambergite	1.555-1.626	± .002	.071	2.35	7½
Petalite	1.502-1.518		.016	2.40	6
Apophylite	1.535-1.537		.002	2.30-2.50 2.40 Normal	4½-5
Obsidian	1.50	± .020	—	2.35-2.55 2.45 Normal	5-5½
Moldavite	1.50	± .01	—	2.36-2.44 2.40 Normal	5½
Leucite	1.508	+ .001 − .004	—	2.50	5½-6
Orthoclase Feldspar	1.518-1.526		.008	2.55-2.57 2.56 Normal	6-6½
Albite Feldspar	1.525-1.536		.011	2.605	6-6½
Iolite	1.542-1.551	+ .045 − .011	.009	2.56-2.66 2.61 Normal	7-7½
Oligoclase Feldspar	1.539-1.547		.008	2.64	6-6½
Quartz	1.544-1.553		.009	2.65-2.67 2.66 Normal	7
Amethyst Quartz	1.544-1.553		.009	2.65-2.67 2.66 Normal	7
Scapolite	1.550-1.572	± .002	.015 to .022	2.62-2.74 2.68 Normal	6½
Labradorite Feldspar	1.559-1.568		.009	2.65-2.75 2.70 Normal	6
Calcite	1.486-1.658		.172	2.69-2.71 2.70 Normal	3
Augelite	1.574-1.588		.014	2.70	5
Beryl	1.577-1.583	± .017	.005 to .009	2.67-2.84 2.72 Normal	7½-8

Name	Refractive Index	Birefringence	Specific Gravity	Hardness
Aquamarine Beryl	1.577-1.583 ± .017	.005 to .009	2.67-2.84 2.72 Normal	7½-8
Emerald Beryl	1.577-1.583 ± .017	.005 to .009	2.67-2.84 2.72 Normal	7½-8
Morganite Beryl	1.577-1.583 ± .017	.005 to .009	2.67-2.84 2.72 Normal	7½-8
Sugilite	1.61	—	2.74	6-6½
Turquoise	1.61	—	2.31-2.84 2.76 Normal	5-6
Beryllonite	1.552-1.562	.010	2.83-2.87 2.85 Normal	5½-6
Prosopite	1.501-1.510 ± .003	.009	2.89	4½
Pollucite	1.520 ± .005	—	2.90-2.94 2.92 Normal	6½
Brazilianite	1.602-1.621 ± .003	.019	2.91-2.97 2.94 Normal	5½
Aragonite	1.530-1.685	.155	2.94	3½-4
Nephrite Jade	1.60	—	2.90-3.00 2.95 Normal	6-6½
Phenakite	1.654-1.670 + .026 − .004	.016	2.94-2.96 2.95 Normal	7½-8
Datolite	1.626-1.670	.044	2.90-3.00 2.95 Normal	5-5½
Danburite	1.630-1.636 ± .003	.006	2.99-3.01 3.00 Normal	7
Amblygonite	1.612-1.636	.024	3.02	6
Tourmaline	1.624-1.644 ± .006	.020	3.01-3.21 3.06 Normal	7-7½
Phosphophylite	1.595-1.616	.021	3.08	3-4
Lazulite	1.612-1.643	.031	3.04-3.14 3.09 Normal	5-6
Actinolite	1.614-1.641 + .014	.025	3.00-3.20 3.10 Normal	5-6
Euclase	1.654-1.673 ± .004	.019	3.09-3.11 3.10 Normal	7½
Andalusite	1.634-1.643 ± .005	.008 to .013	3.13-3.21 3.17 Normal	7-7½
Spodumene	1.660-1.676 ± .005	.016	3.15-3.21 3.18 Normal	6-7
Hiddenite Spodumene	1.660-1.676 ± .005	.016	3.15-3.21 3.18 Normal	6-7
Kunzite Spodumene	1.660-1.676 ± .005	.016	3.15-3.21 3.18 Normal	6-7
Apatite	1.642-1.646 + .005 − .014	.002 to .006	3.16-3.20 3.18 Normal	5
Fluorite	1.434	—	3.17-3.19 3.18 Normal	4
Clinozoisite	1.724-1.734 − .090	.010	3.21-3.38	6½

Name	Refractive Index		Birefringence	Specific Gravity	Hardness
Sillimanite	1.659-1.680		.015 to .021	3.22-3.26 3.24 Normal	6-7
Enstatite	1.658-1.668	± .005	.010	3.23-3.27 3.25 Normal	5½
Ekanite	1.597		—	3.28	6-6½
Diopside	1.675-1.701	+ .029 − .010	.026	3.26-3.32 3.29 Normal	5-6
Axinite	1.678-1.688	± .005	.010	3.27-3.31 3.29 Normal	6½-7
Tanzanite Zoisite	1.691-1.704	± .003	.013	3.20-3.40 3.30 Normal	6-7
Dumortierite	1.678-1.689		.011	3.20-3.40 3.30 Normal	7
Dioptase	1.655-1.708	± .012	.053	3.25-3.35 3.30 Normal	5
Kornerupine	1.667-1.680	± .003	.013	3.25-3.35 3.30 Normal	6½
Jadeite Jade	1.66		—	3.30-3.38 3.34 Normal	6½-7
Peridot	1.654-1.690	± .020	.036	3.31-3.48 3.34 Normal	6½-7
Rhodizite	1.69		—	3.40	8
Idocrase	1.713-1.718	± .013	.005	3.30-3.50 3.40 Normal	6½
Epidote	1.729-1.768	+ .012 − .035	.019 to .045	3.32-3.48 3.40 Normal	6-7
Hemimorphite	1.614-1.636		.022	3.40-3.50 3.45 Normal	4½-5
Sinhalite	1.668-1.707	± .003	.039	3.46-3.50 3.48 Normal	6-7
Sphene	1.900-2.034	± .020	.10 to .135	3.50-3.54 3.52 Normal	5-5½
Diamond	2.417		—	3.51-3.53 3.52 Normal	10
Topaz	1.619-1.627	± .010	.008	3.49-3.57 3.53 Normal	8
Spinel	1.718	+ .044 − .006	—	3.57-3.90 3.60 Normal	8
Taaffeite	1.719-1.723	− .002	.004 to .005	3.61	8
Tsavorite Garnet	1.74	± .01	—	3.57-3.73 3.61 Normal	7
Grossular Garnet	1.74	± .01	—	3.57-3.73 3.61 Normal	7
Hessonite Garnet	1.74	± .01	—	3.57-3.73 3.61 Normal	7
Kyanite	1.716-1.731	± .004	.015	3.56-3.68 3.62 Normal	4-7
Benitoite	1.757-1.804		.047	3.61-3.67 3.64 Normal	6-6½
Rhodochrosite	1.597-1.817	± .003	.220	3.70	3½-4½

Name	Refractive Index	Birefringence	Specific Gravity	Hardness
Staurolite	1.736-1.746	.010	3.65-3.77 / 3.71 Normal	7-7½
Alexandrite Chrysoberyl	1.746-1.755 ±.005	.009	3.71-3.75 / 3.73 Normal	8½
Cat's-eye Chrysoberyl	1.746-1.755 ±.005	.009	3.71-3.75 / 3.73 Normal	8½
Chrysoberyl	1.746-1.755 ±.005	.009	3.71-3.75 / 3.73 Normal	8½
Pyrope Garnet	1.746 +.010 −.026	—	3.62-3.87 / 3.78 Normal	7-7½
Azurite	1.73-1.84 ±.010	.11	3.30-3.87 / 3.80 Normal	3½-4
Rhodolite Garnet	1.760 ±.010	—	3.74-3.94 / 3.84 Normal	7-7½
Demantoid Garnet	1.875 ±.020	—	3.81-3.87 / 3.84 Normal	6½-7
Willemite	1.691-1.719	.028	3.90-4.10 / 4.00 Normal	5½
Zircon (low)	1.810-1.815 ±.030	.002 to .005	3.93-4.07 / 4.00 Normal	6½
Ruby Corundum	1.762-1.770 +.008 −.003	.008	3.97-4.03 / 4.00 Normal	9
Sapphire Corundum	1.762-1.770 +.008 −.003	.008	3.97-4.03 / 4.00 Normal	9
Gahnite	1.80	—	4.0-4.6	7½
Painite	1.787-1.816	.029	4.01	8
Gahnospinel	1.76	—	3.61-4.41 / 4.01 Normal	7½
Almandite Garnet	1.79 ±.030	—	3.93-4.17 / 4.05 Normal	7½
Sphalerite	2.37	—	4.03-4.07 / 4.05 Normal	3½-4
Spessartite Garnet	1.81 ±.010	—	4.12-4.18 / 4.15 Normal	7-7½
Rutile	2.616-2.903	.287	4.24-4.28 / 4.26 Normal	6-6½
Zircon (medium)	1.875-1.905 ±.030	.006 to .050	4.07-4.57 / 4.32 Normal	7½
Barite	1.636-1.648	.012	4.50	3-3½
Y.A.G. (Yttrium Aluminum Garnet)	1.833	—	4.55	8¼
Linobate	2.21-2.30	.09	4.64	5½
Zircon (high)	1.925-1.984 ±.040	.059	4.67-4.73 / 4.70 Normal	7½
Strontium Titanate	2.409	—	5.11-5.15 / 5.13 Normal	5-6
Cubic Zirconia	2.15	—	5.60-5.95	8-8½

Name	Refractive Index	Birefringence	Specific Gravity	Hardness
Zincite	2.013-2.029	.016	5.70	4-4½
Scheelite	1.918-1.934	0.16	6.12	5
Wulfenite	2.28-2.40	.12	6.5-7.0	2¾-3
Cassiterite	1.997-2.098 +.008 −.006	.096	6.87-7.03 6.95 Normal	6-7
G.G.G. (Gadolinium Gallium Garnet)	2.03	—	7.05	6½
Stibiotantalite	2.37-2.45	.08	7.20-7.80 7.50 Normal	5

GLOSSARY

A

Absorption -- portions of the spectrum contained by white light may be subtracted when that light passes through a gemstone, while other components of the spectrum pass through leaving a particular identifiable color.

Absorption spectrum -- the pattern of dark lines and colors formed by the absorption of certain components of white light passing through a gemstone which can be observed with a spectroscope.

Alface -- a Portuguese word meaning lettuce, used to describe a pale green color in tourmaline.

Alluvial -- soil, gravel, sometimes including gem gravel which is deposited by running water.

Appraisal -- in our context the value placed on a given gemstone in money by an appraiser.

Axis -- in our use, crystal axis, a term used in crystallography; an axis is a hypothetical line about which a solid figure is symmetrical. All crystals have more than one axis. The use of the term axis is an attempt by mineralogists to describe minerals in relation to solid geometry.

B

Bi-colored -- a stone of two colors -- as distinguished from a stone exhibiting true dichroism.

Birefringence -- the measure of double refraction; it is the greatest difference between the refractive indices passing through doubly refractive material.

Body color -- the color of a gemstone as caused by transmitted light as opposed to reflected or refracted light.

Brilliancy -- the amount of light reaching the eye as a result of reflections from the internal surfaces of the facets of a gemstone; the amount of light returned to the eye from the facets below the girdle.

Brilliant cut -- the most popular cut for diamonds; specifically the round brilliant cut which has a round girdle outline and usually has 58 facets; 32 facets and a table are above the girdle while 24 facets and a culet are below. Quite often the culet facet is omitted in which case the stone has only 57 facets.

Bubble veils -- this term is actually a misnomer. These are veil-like inclusions which appear to be made of bubbles but which are actually made of small crystalline inclusions. However the visual cue created by the term bubble veils is much closer to the appearance of these inclusions.

C

Cabochon cut -- a gemstone with a smooth unfaceted dome on top which is polished. The back of the cabochon cut stone (also unfaceted) can either be polished or unpolished, flat, concave or slightly convex.

Carat -- a standard unit of weight used for weighing gemstones; a carat equals 200 milligrams and is further divided into 100 points. Five carats = one gram.

Cat's - eye -- a cabochon cut stone exhibiting a line of light across the upper dome of the stone. The term cat's-eye classically refers to chrysoberyl cat's-eye; however, there are several other minerals from which cat's-eye gems can be fashioned, including tourmaline, beryl and even opal. With the exception of opal, the cat's-eye phenomenon is a result of the reflection of light off parallel needle-like crystal inclusions.

Certificate -- in gemology, a written document that a stone is of a certain species, color, weight and other characteristics acceptable or not acceptable for the species in question. A certificate can also have a dollar valuation or not have a dollar valuation.

Clarity -- in gemology the extent to which a stone is or is not included, that is, whether or not the stone has inclusions and the extent to which those inclusions exist in the stone.

Cleavage -- the characteristic of a crystalline mineral to part in certain directions with regard to the crystal axis; a cleavage tends to leave a smooth somewhat polished looking surface. Cleavage always occurs in a plane.

Cobbing -- in reference to gemstone mining, it is the process of removing undesirable parts of the gemstone through the use of a hammer, sometimes a large hammer in large, low quality gemstones or sometimes the use of a small, fine hammer for more expensive gemstone rough.

Cloud-like inclusions -- an inclusion which is actually made up of a grouping of small inclusions which has the appearance of a three-dimensional cloud or foggy appearance.

Color -- a visible property of light; in gemstones the color can be either reflected, refracted, or transmitted from the gemstone. Color only occurs in the visible wavelengths of light. Color can also refer to the name of a particular hue.

Color blindness -- the lack of ability to discern certain colors or the differences between certain colors; sometimes the inability to perceive any color at all other than black and white and the accompanying shades of gray in between.

Colored stones -- this is somewhat of a trade jargon that is used to classify any gemstone of any species other than diamonds. Ironically, some of these species do produce colorless gemstones, yet these are lumped together under the umbrella of colored stones. Whether to include or to exclude colored diamonds is a somewhat unresolved situation.

Colorless stones -- in gemology, stones without color of any kind.

Crown -- that portion of a faceted gemstone above the girdle.

Crystallography -- the study of crystal composition and formation.

Culet -- a small facet placed at the tip of the pavilion of a round stone or across the knife edge of the pavilion of an emerald cut stone.

Cut -- as a verb, the word cut refers to the fashioning of a gemstone from the rough to a finished piece. As a noun, the word cut refers to the particular form which that fashioning has created; specifically a round cut, a pear-shaped cut, an emerald cut, a marquise cut and so forth.

D

Dark-field illumination -- a method of lighting gemstones used specifically for viewing inclusions. Dark-field illumination uses a powerful light from the sides of the gemstone while the eye views the gemstone against a dark background.

Dichroism -- a characteristic of most doubly refractive colored stones of either the tetragonal or hexagonal crystal systems whereby two different colors are transmitted in two different directions.

Dichroscope -- a gemological tool which enables a viewer to discern the different colors transmitted through dichroic or trichroic gemstones.

Doublet -- a gemstone formed from two separate pieces of material which are cemented together to make one stone.

Double refraction -- the separation of a single ray of light into two rays vibrating at right angles to each other. After separation the two rays travel at different speeds and are differently absorbed by the mineral in which they are traveling.

E

Eye-clean -- a trade term referring to a stone which appears to be without inclusions or other flaws when viewed without the aid of optical instruments.

F

Facet -- the plane, geometric polished faces which are fashioned on a gemstone.

F.G.A. -- Fellow Gemmological Association; a title awarded by the Gemmological Association of Great Britain to persons who have successfully completed their required course in the study of gemmology.

Fire -- in faceted stones, a layman's term for dispersion. In regard to opals, the term fire is also used in place of the term "play of color".

Flawless -- the absence of inclusions, blemishes, internal cleavage or fractures in a gemstone.

Flaws -- inclusions of foreign minerals, internal cleavages, fractures or blemishes visible in a gemstone.

Fractures -- parting that occurs within a stone. In stones which exhibit cleavage, fractures refer to parting in directions other than those parallel to the cleavage plane or planes.

"Freebie" appraisal -- trade jargon referring to what persons frequently want when they are curious as to the worth of a stone they have acquired and do not want to pay an appraisal fee.

G

Gemstones -- any precious stone which can be refined by cutting and polishing for use in jewelry or for collecting purposes.

Girdle -- that part of a gemstone existing in a plane separating the crown and pavilion of a gemstone. The girdle is parallel to the table of the gemstone and is the part of the stone with the greatest diameter.

Grading -- arranging in order of size, quality, color, cut, and other pre-determined specifications assigned to a specific variety of gemstones.

H

Heavy liquids -- liquids having high specific gravity in which various stones either sink or float; float if their specific gravity is lower; sink if their specific gravity is higher; used to identify one gem species from similar stones and/or synthetics or imitations.

Hue -- the name of a color such as pink, orange, yellow, green; also the characteristic by which a color is distinguished from black, white, or neutral gray.

I

Immersion cell -- a colorless container (usually glass) used to immerse a gemstone in order to eliminate reflection from the surface to be better able to observe the interior of the stone.

Inclusion -- a substance enclosed within a gemstone which is visible to either the naked eye or with magnification.

M

Master stone or stones -- a single stone or set of stones which are representative of a specified quality and of certain characteristics in a particular species; used in determining if the stone in question measures up to the standards and in what way.

Melee -- originally a French word which is used to describe small, round, faceted stones less than .25 carats. Melee stones are quite often used in jewelry as side stones for larger gems.

Metamorphic -- a geologic term used to describe rock which was originally formed in one type of geologic occurrence, later submerged under the surface of the earth and reformed or metamorphosed by the pressure at the depths at which it was submerged, then later re-emerged to the surface.

Microscope -- in our case, a gemological instrument either monocular or binocular with high magnification for use in observing minute characteristics of gemstones such as inclusions.

Mineral -- any of a class of substances occurring in nature, comprised of inorganic material of definite chemical composition.

Monochromatic -- consisting of one single color.

N

Needles -- in our context, inclusions in a stone comprised of small needle-like crystals, usually either of rutile or actinolite.

O

Open cleavages -- cracks parallel to the cleavage planes in a rough or cut gem material; when reflected through the stone, an open cleavage will give off a shiny appearance. Open cleavages should be cut out of finished gemstones.

Overtones -- in our context, a second, less important hue observed in the body color of a gemstone.

Opaque stones -- gemstones which transmit no light as opposed to transparent gemstones which do transmit light.

P

Pavilion -- that part of a gemstone which is positioned below the girdle when the gemstone is held in its normal observing position.

Pegmatite -- a type of geologic formation; pegmatites are a type of igneous rock; associated with pegmatites are many of the silicate gem minerals such as tourmaline, beryl, topaz, quartz and spodumene.

Pleochroism -- the two or three-color effect a doubly refractive mineral may have when the rays of light are differentially absorbed and the wavelength is changed.

Pleochroic -- demonstrating the effect of pleochroism.

Point -- in our context, used to mean 100th of one carat; 100 points equals one (1) carat when weighing gemstones.

Polariscope -- a gemological instrument utilizing polarized light for determining whether a stone is singly or doubly refractive.

Polarizing filter -- a filter which limits light vibrations to parallel planes in contrast with ordinary light which vibrates in all planes at right angles to its direction of movement.

Proportionscope -- a product of Gem Instruments Corporation used in diamond grading. It projects the stone's image on a screen for comparison with an ideal image of a round, brilliant diamond which is permanently affixed to the screen.

R

Rare -- unusual, uncommon; occurring far apart in time.

Reflection -- in our context, that light which returns after striking the external or internal facets of a stone.

Refraction -- bending of the direction of travel of a light ray line as it passes from one medium to another, such as from air to a gemstone.

Refractive index -- in our context, the measure of the amount a light ray bends as it enters or leaves a gemstone; by using a table of refractive indices, gemstones can, in certain cases, be identified and classified by species and synthetics determined.

Refractometer -- in our context, a gemological instrument used for measuring the refractive indices of gemstones, often used in conjunction with a table of refractive indices.

Retail -- sale of goods to the ultimate consumer; retail prices are commonly the highest price paid for any given commodity.

Rutile -- a mineral primarily consisting of titanium dioxide; it is of note in regard to gemstones as an inclusion in other gemstones although occasionally rutile can be found in crystals large enough to be faceted for rare-gemstone collectors.

S

Saturation -- entirely soaked or imbued, as with a single color free from any mixture of any other color. Degree of color saturation is often one quality used in determining the value of a gemstone. Saturated colors in gemstones tend to be prized.

Scintillation -- in our context, flashes of bright light reflected off the external surface of facets.

Shade -- in out context, the increments of color ranging from light to dark as in one stone being a slight one shade lighter or darker than another.

Silk -- small, needle-like inclusions in a stone which run parallel to each other of which light is reflected in such a way as to produce a whitish or blue-white shine or sheen. Silk inclusions are responsible for the chatoyancy of cat's-eye stones and the asterism in star stones. The term silk is in reference to the appearance of the inclusion, not its composition.

Single refraction -- as differs from double refraction, the normal manner in which a ray of light is refracted when entering a crystal. Light is not divided into two rays as it passes from air into a mineral.

"Sleepy" stone -- stones which, due to existence of many small inclusions, do not exhibit the normal brilliancy of stones of the same variety.

Species -- the mineralogical division of gemstones; gemstones of one species all share the same scientific characteristics.

Specific gravity -- gemologically, it is the ratio of density of a gemstone to that of water at 4°C or 36°F.

Spectroscope -- a gemological instrument used for identifying gemstones based on comparative absorption.

Starring -- a phenomenon in gemstones consisting of four to twelve rays of two or more intersecting bands of light; caused by reflection of light from groups of oriented needle-like inclusions; stones must be cut en cabochon for this phenomenon to be observed. Starring is also known as asterism.

Synthetic -- pertaining to compounds produced artificially in a laboratory by chemical reaction; not authentic or genuine; man-made.

T

Table -- the large, flat facet on the crown of a faceted gemstone which is parallel with the girdle of a gemstone.

Thermal reaction tester -- an instrument used to indicate the heat conductivity of stones; especially helpful in determining diamonds from diamond simulates.

Tone -- a characteristic of color which has to do with its position on a scale of light to dark, much the same as the word shade.

Translucent stones -- stones which transmit light only partially.

Trichroism -- a characteristic of certain doubly refractive colored gemstones. Trichroic stones transmit three different colors along each of the three crystal axes. These are characteristic of the orthorhombic, monoclinic and triclinic crystal systems.

Tri-colored stones -- having three distinct colors; not to be confused with trichroism.

Triplet -- an assembled stone of three parts bound together.

Tubular inclusions -- long, hollow cylindrical inclusions common to tourmaline, beryl, spodumene, but occurring in other gem species.

Twinning -- the growth process by which two crystals are joined together along a common axis or plane.

V

Value -- in color, the relative effect of color especially with reference to the degree of lightness and darkness.

W

Windowed stone -- a stone improperly cut so that you see through it rather than seeing reflections off the back facets.

Wispy veils -- translucent inclusions resembling gossamer cloth.

SUGGESTED READING:
Gem Books

The Book of Opals

Wilfred Eyles
Charles E. Tuttle, Rutland, Vermont & Tokyo, Japan (1964)

Graphics: Black & White and Color Photographs; Maps

Synopsis: This book discusses all aspects of the opal very comprehensively, including mining locations in Australia and Rainbow Ridge in Nevada. Mining methods, geological and gem field formations are reviewed. The author talks about dealer methods of trading opals, color, cutting techniques and includes information on the types of equipment needed for this cutting.

He also discusses preservation of opals and some of the more common opal peculiarities and superstitions attached to opals.

The Curious Lore of Precious Stones

George Kunz
Halcyon House, New York (1938)

Graphics: Color Photographs; Black & White Photographs; Sketches

Synopsis: This book is described on the title page as "being a description of their sentiments and folk lore superstitions, symbolism, mysticism, use in medicine, protection, prevention, religion, and divination, crystal gazing, birthstones, lucky stones and talismans, astral, zodiacal and planetary."

The book primarily discusses precious stones as used by various peoples in different places and especially the way in which stones have been used and seen as a source of mystery. The author describes in depth some of the fancies and superstitions which have surrounded gemstones in ancient times, especially in connection with religion, medicine, and astrology.

Dictionary of Gems and Gemology

Robert M. Shipley
Gemological Institute of America, Los Angeles (1974)

Graphics: None

Synopsis: A compact, all-inclusive reference work for the layman or beginning student. Contains definitions of most commonly used gemological terms, especially designed for the study of colored stones, pearls and their substitutes. Includes a listing with descriptions of organizations, periodicals, laboratories, and museums concerned with gems.

Faberge: Court Jeweler to the Tsar

G. Von Habsburg-Lothringen & A. von Solodkoff
Rizzoli International Publications, Inc., New York (1979)

Graphics: Black & White and Color Plates

Synopsis: A very comprehensive book on the art and works of Carl Faberge. Includes chapters on the history of the House of Faberge, with a discussion on style, techniques, revivals, imitators, and fakes.

The book discusses in detail the famous Easter Egg collection and the gems and jewels designed for the Tsars of Russia. A unique feature of this book are several sales ledgers for Christie's Auction House from the period 1907-1917, which gives some interesting comparisons between costs and sale prices of that era.

This volume bases its information both on traditional sources and some new sources, especially unpublished photographs from private collections and the archives of Christie's. An analysis of the market then and now and the role of dealers and collectors comes under discussion.

The color works in this volume are especially beautiful and detailed.

Faberge -- Goldsmith to the Imperial Court

1846-1920
A. Kenneth Snowman
Debrett's Purage Ltd., in association with the Victoria and Albert Museum (1977)

Graphics: Color and Black & White Photographs

Synopsis: A catalog put together for the Jubilee of Elizabeth II of England which emphasizes the works of Faberge which have been collected by the British Royal Family. These pieces are considered of more interest because Faberge designed them for pleasure and did not have to give thought to price or their speculative value. The collection includes works owned by Queen Elizabeth II, Prince Charles, and Queen Alexandra. Especially interesting are the tiny animals from the Queen Alexandra collection; she being the sister of the Russian Dowager Empress.

The book has a history of the collection, notes on materials, enamels and stones used by Faberge. It lists marks and standards and the work masters' marks.

Each photograph has an accompanying description of the object in question, and which member of the Royal Family lent it.

Gem and Crystal Treasures

Peter Bancroft
Western Enterprises, Fallbrook, CA (1984)

Graphics: Black & White Photographs, Color Plates

Synopsis: 100 chapters of the world's 100 classic crystal producing locations with emphasis on the history and lore of these famous worldwide deposits. The book is not only beautifully executed but promises to infect the reader with all the excitement that gem mining and gem mystery can create. Ideal for people interested in the production of gem mines and the mineral specimens they produce.

Gem & Gem Materials

Edward Krause, Ph.D., Sc.D. and Chester Slawson, Ph.D.
McGraw-Hill Book Co., Inc. New York and London (1941)

Graphics: Black & White Photographs; Charts; Sketches

Synopsis: Divided into three parts; deals with the description, properties and characteristics of colored gemstones, diamonds, metallic gem minerals and organic gem materials.

Part I discusses the physical, optical, and chemical properties of gems, including how gems occur. This section also deals with the cutting and polishing of gemstones; manufacture and naming of gems; and metals used in mounting.

Part II is devoted entirely to descriptions of individual gemstones, including precious, semi-precious, minerals and organic materials.

Part III classifies gem materials according to various properties such as hardness, specific gravity, optical properties, refractive indices, etc.

The book includes various tables and indices which are both helpful and useful.

Gems and Precious Stones of North America

George F. Kunz
Dover Publications, Inc., New York 1968

Graphics: Color Plates; Black & White Photographs; Charts; Sketches

Synopsis: To quote the title page of this volume, "A popular description of their occurrences, value, history, archaeology, and of the collections in which they exist, also a chapter on pearls and on remarkable foreign gems owned in the United States."

This book should prove useful to gem and mineral collectors, lapidary artists, hobbyists, rockhounds, and lay persons interested in learning about gems and their history in North America. Discusses where and how gemstones are found in the United States, Canada and Mexico. Sections on how stones are mined and the value of production of different stones is included.

Chapters are broken down by various gemstone groups such as diamond, corundum, turquoise, topaz, garnet. In these chapters a complete description and analysis of the gems is given. Pearls and minerals which are made into art objects are also included.

Gemstones of North America

John Sinkankas
D. Van Nostrand Co., Inc., Princeton, New Jersey (1959)
VOL. II 1976

Graphics: Black & White and Color Photographs and Line Drawings

Synopsis: This comprehensive volume reviews gemstone sources in North America, including the most popular stones and those which, due to rarity or softness, are not so popular. A complete, comprehensive and detailed book can be used by students, collectors, and professionals. Emphasizes which stones can be found where in North America and in what quantities and qualities.

The book includes a basic introduction to terminology, leading to a discussion of individual stones and mineral species, including pearl, amber, jet and coral. The in-depth discussion includes scientific optical properties.

Sinkankas has listed the gems in order of importance to the trade and jewelry business. He also has included a chapter on massive and decorative gemstones which covers such items as granite, unakite, muscovite mica and obsidian, lapis lazuli, fluorite, among others.

A glossary and index to locations completes this volume.

Gemstones of the World

Walter Schumann (Translated by Evelyne Stern, FGA)
Sterling Publishing Co., Inc., New York & Press Limited, London, England (1977-English)

Graphics: Color Plates; Charts; Sketches

Synopsis: This text provides many complete and detailed charts and tables pertaining to the gemstone world. Gemstones are discussed scientifically in terms of formation and structure; properties; deposits and production of gems and cutting and polishing. Also included are chapters on synthetics and gem classification.

One entire chapter is devoted to a description of major gemstones, with a section on gems for collectors included, both common and rare varieties.

The book concludes with chapters on organic materials and diamond production.

The color plates in this text are of particularly fine quality and very representative of the gemstone field.

In the sections under description, each stone is outlined in the major areas of interest such as color, hardness, cleavage, dispersion, etc.

Great Treasures of the Kremlin

David Duncan
Harry N. Abrams, Inc., New York (1967)

Graphics: Color Photographs

Synopsis: Russia and her history from ancient times through the Revolution of 1917 is explored through the gems and jewels of the Russian people.

The book contains over 100 color photographs, beginning with the ancient Monomakh Cap and describing 13 other royal crowns and the details of the gems in their settings. The Russians were noted not only for using gems in royal objects but also for many common objects such as horse armament, knives, helmets, dishes, book covers, etc.

This book describes such jewels as turquoise, pearls, ruby, and topaz in detail.

Handbook of Gem Identification

Richard T. Liddicoat, Jr.
Gem Instruments of America, Los Angeles, California (1953)

Graphics: Black & White Photographs, Charts, Tables

Synopsis: The first ten chapters are a detailed discussion of the physical, optical, and characteristic properties of gemstones. This description includes such items as inclusions, specific gravity, pleochroism, and hardness.

These chapters also include discussions of identification by characteristic properties such as inclusions; doublets, foil backs, and which are synthetic stones. There is a chapter on pearls and their properties.

After a description of gem instruments and their uses, individual gemstone identification is presented by color and substitutes are identified.

Jewelry: Ancient to Modern

A Studio Book by the Walters Art Gallery, Baltimore
Viking Press, New York (1979)

Graphics: Color and Black & White Plates

Synopsis: This book in reality represents a gallery catalog of the Walters Art Gallery of Baltimore. It represents jewelry through a period of 6,000 years, from simple stone Egyptian amulets to Tiffany creations of the 20th century.

Over 700 pieces from the ancient near east Egypt, Etruria, Greece, South Russia, and the Roman Empire are represented. In addition, the collection includes pieces from the migration period, Byzantine Empire, Middle Ages, Renaissance, and the 18th, 19th and 20th centuries.

The volume contains 95% color plates with detailed historical and other pertinent data being described in connection with each piece.

Mystical Jewels of the Middle Ages and the Renaissance

Joan Evans
Dover Publications Inc. New York (1976)

Graphics: Black & White Photographs

Synopsis: Deals with the religious and magical aspects attributed to gems from ancient times to the 17th century and how a people's culture was affected by these magical properties.

The work draws on ancient writings, inscriptions, and religious beliefs. There is an appendix of transcripts in the original Latin.

The Opal Book

Frank Leechman, FGA
Ure Smith Pty. Limited, Sydney, Australia (1961)

Graphics: Black & White and Color Photographs and Plates; Charts; Tables; Sketches

Synopsis: A book designed for use by both the scientist and lay person as a reference guide to opals. The book discusses the foreign opal fields, with a special emphasis on the early days of opal mining in Australia. Further descriptions are given of the ancient history and myth of opals, their discovery in Australia and how opal forms in both lava-rock and sandstone deserts.

There is a rather complete section of mining methods and varieties of opal mined. Following this the uses of opal are discussed -- how the gem is cut, shaped and polished, uses as a precious gem, care of and imitations to watch out for.

The author also includes a unique chapter on "the latest information of the cause of color in opal ... which dispels the outmoded theories that are still being taught and that still appear in print."

Practical Gemmology

Robert Webster, FGA
N.A.G. Press, Ltd., London, England (1st Ed. 1943)

Graphics: Black & White Photographs; Graphs; Sketches

Synopsis: This text is a beginner's guide to the study of gemstones, pearls, and ornamental minerals. Although it was designed to be a companion volume to the author's *Pocket Compendium,* no special scientific knowledge is required.

Here we list the subjects covered by lesson:

Introduction
Crystallography
Physical Properties
Specific Gravity
Measurement of Refractive Index
Imitation Gems
Composite Stones and Artificially
    Induced Color
Styles of Cutting
Testing a Parcel of Stones

Color in Gem Distinction
Microscope
Gem Species
Synthetic Gems
Ornamental Minerals
The Pearl
Coral, Amber, Jet
Tortoiseshell and Ivory
Unusual Gemstones

Precious Stones

Dr. Max Bauer
Translated by L.J. Spencer, M.A, (Cantab.), FGA
Charles E. Tuttle Company, Rutland, Vermont & Tokyo, Japan (1969)

Graphics: Color Plates; Charts; Sketches

Synopsis: Described as a popular account of the character, occurrence, and application of precious stones, with an introduction to their determination, this book can be used by mineralogists, lapidaries, jewelers and students. An appendix on pearls and coral is included.

The text, a very complete volume, divides into three parts. Part I deals with the general characteristics of precious stones, physical properties, optical properties and thermal, electrical and magnetic characters. Also included in this section is a description of the technical and jewelry applications of gemstones.

The second part is devoted to an in-depth description and study of over 75 precious stones and minerals.

Determination and distinguishing of precious stones -- transparent, colored, translucent and opaque, is the topic of the third part.

In the final appendices synthetic gems and cultured pearls are discussed.

The System of Mineralogy of James D. Dana and Edward S. Dana

Seventh Edition
Charles Palache, Harry Barman, and Cliford Frondel
John Wiley & Sons, Inc., New York, London, and Sydney

Graphics: Charts; Graphs; Tables

Synopsis: This textbook by the late Danas is a complete, detailed set in three volumes on mineralogy, updated to take into account the most recent scientific discoveries regarding minerals. The introduction outlines these changes in light of the new information.

Minerals are discussed in view of their properties, chemistry, optical properties, cell structure, habit, where found, crystallography, etc.

255

The volumes are broken down as follows:

Volume I   Elements, Sulfides, Sulfosalts, Oxides
Volume II   Halides, Nitrates, Borates, Carbonates, Sulfates,
                          Phosphates, Arsenates, Tungstates, Molybdates,
                          etc.
Volume III   Silica Minerals

These volumes are technical and scientific in their approach, using scientific notation, chemistry language, and providing sophisticated charts and graphs.

A Textbook of Mineralogy with an Extended Treatise on Crystallography & Physical Mineralogy

By Edward Dana
Fourth Edition, revised by William E. Ford
John Wiley & Sons, Inc., New York, London, Sydney (1949)

Graphics: Graphs; Tables; Sketches

Synopsis: This book is a textbook which gives in great detail information about the inorganic species called minerals which have chemical compositions and definite atomic structures. Definitions, and detailed charts and graphs are provided. The text is written in a scientific manner.

A description of the four parts of this book will give the reader a sample of the kind of information contained therein.

I. Crystallography -- detailed analysis by systems, including the most common ones.

II. Physical Mineralogy -- discussion of characteristics dependent on light, optics, heat, electricity and magnetism.

III. Chemical Mineralogy -- general principles of chemistry as applied to minerals is discussed.

IV. Descriptive Mineralogy -- description of the minerals discussed by their mineralogical name such as silicates, oxides, carbonates, etc.

256

There are two appendices. The first deals with drawings of crystal figures and the second lists tables to be used in the determination of minerals, general index, and an index to species.

A Treasury of Jewels and Gems

Mona Curran
Emerson Books, Inc., New York (1962)

Graphics: Black & White Photographs

Synopsis: The 32 photographs in this book describe the background and history of famous stones, tracing the development of various jewelry styles, sources and care of jewels.

The book is laid out in terms of types of jewelry, such as rings, brooches, necklaces and earrings. There are chapters on types of settings and cuttings, plus period jewelry and birthstones.

A special chapter discusses the Crown Jewels of England and those owned personally by Queen Elizabeth II.

A section to the technical aspects of jeweled stones, appraising, cutting, and polishing.

How the more popular stones are mined, marketed and where found is also discussed.

INDEX

259

NOTES

NOTES

NOTES

NOTES